INTERACTIVE READER
VOLUME A

Secondary System

Authors

Nancy E. Marchand-Martella
Ronald C. Martella
Douglas Fisher
Jay McTighe
Marcia Kosanovich
Mina Johnson-Glenberg
Ernest Morrell

Bothell, WA • Chicago, IL • Columbus, OH • New York, NY

www.*FLEX*Literacy.com

 **Education**

Copyright © 2014 The McGraw-Hill Companies, Inc.

All rights reserved. No part of this publication may be
reproduced or distributed in any form or by any means, or
stored in a database or retrieval system, without the prior
written consent of The McGraw-Hill Companies, Inc.,
including, but not limited to, network storage or
transmission, or broadcast for distance learning.

Send all inquiries to:
McGraw-Hill Education
8787 Orion Place
Columbus, OH 43240

ISBN: 978-0-07-661583-4
MHID: 0-07-661583-9

Printed in the United States of America.

1 2 3 4 5 6 7 8 9 QDB 17 16 15 14 13 12

Contents

Contents

The Gift of the Magi

By O. Henry
Retold by Arden Davidson

Build Background

Word:

Definition:

....

....

....

....

Word:

Definition:

....

....

....

....

....

It was Christmas Eve. The snow had fallen. The cold had settled in comfortably. And so had Della, a beautiful young woman, who sat in her small apartment counting her change. "Eighty-five, eighty-six, eighty-seven," she said aloud as she stacked the last of her pennies. Her grand total was $1.87. All the saving and hard work she had endured these last few months had resulted in a **mere** $1.87.

She tried to comfort herself. But she could not. Della was so disappointed she flung herself onto her old, worn sofa and began to cry. A spring popped up and almost cut her. That made her cry even harder.

Della was sad with good reason. She wanted to buy a really nice Christmas present for her husband, Jim. The couple was quite poor. They did not have many fancy things. But Della wanted to show Jim her love with a special gift. Sadly, she knew that $1.87 would not do.

Della wanted badly to buy Jim a fancy chain for his gold pocket watch. Jim truly loved that watch! He would pull it out whenever he could. He didn't really care what time it was. He just wanted to show off his most prized possession. He also wanted to admire it himself.

Generate Questions

....

....

....

....

The only problem was that Jim had only a torn leather strap to attach the watch to his pocket. It just didn't seem right. It was like combining silk sheets with burlap pillows. The watch was far too elegant for the strap that held it.

Della felt that Jim deserved a lovely gold chain that was worthy of his lovely gold watch. But $1.87 would not pay even for a shoestring. And this was why Della cried. She wanted to make her husband happy. She wanted to give him the perfect Christmas gift. She just had to think of some way to buy that chain!

So Della sat and thought. Then she thought some more. As she was twirling her hair around her finger, the idea finally hit her. She jumped up and yelled, "Yes!"

It was twirling her hair that had given her the idea. Della loved her hair as much as Jim loved his watch. She was so proud of the way it flowed down to her ankles. She loved to show it off. And she smiled at the **envy** of others. But as much as she loved her hair, Della loved her husband even more. That was why she did what she did next.

The Gift of the Magi

Della knew of a store that bought hair and made it into wigs. She already had $1.87. She needed only twenty dollars more. "That will be just enough to buy that twenty-one-dollar chain for Jim," Della told herself. She walked into the store feeling proud. An hour later she came out with $21.87 in her pocket and very short hair. An hour after that she was back at home with eighty-seven cents and a wonderful gift for her husband. Della was worried about what Jim would think about her new haircut. But mostly she was happy she had a special Christmas gift to give him.

Della waited anxiously for Jim to arrive home. When she heard the doorknob turn, she was excited. But when Jim saw his wife's short hair, all he could do was stare. He looked like he had just been punched in the stomach.

"It will grow back fast," Della quickly told Jim. She did not know what he was thinking. "I'm sorry if you don't like it, but I did it for you."

Jim finally snapped out of his trance. He told Della she looked beautiful, no matter what. Then he gave her a kiss on the cheek for comfort. "Forgive me for staring," Jim said. "You will understand my **reaction** when you open your gift." He handed Della a small box with a bow.

Generate Questions

The Gift of the Magi

When Della opened the box, she almost **fainted.** Jim had bought her beautiful tortoise-shell combs for her hair. They were the perfect gift. Or, they would have been, if she had not sold her hair. But when she remembered that her hair would soon grow back, Della was once again thrilled about her gift.

She then handed Jim his gift and watched with anticipation as he opened it. All he could do was laugh. "Don't you like it?" Della asked, completely confused by his reaction.

"I love it!" he said. "But I sold my watch to buy you the combs!"

At that point Della could not help but join in with her husband's laughter. They had both given up their most prized possessions to show each other their love. But the gift they had received was so much more special than anything that could be bought in a store. Della and Jim knew from that moment on that their love was real and that their happiness together would last forever.

Verify Prediction

○ **CORRECT**

○ **INCORRECT**

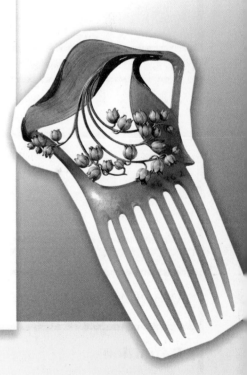

Summarize

_____

_____

_____

_____

_____

Vocabulary Review

Word 1

Definition

Word 2

Definition

Word 3

Definition

Word 4

Definition

	Active Participation	Interactive Reader	Critical Thinking Application	Week 1 Total
TOTAL POINTS FOR WEEK 1				

Anything

But Typical

PART ONE

By Nora Raleigh Baskin

● FICTION
● NONFICTION

Build Background

Most people like to talk in their own language.

They so strongly **prefer** it that when they go to a foreign country they just talk louder, maybe slower, because they think they will be better understood. But more than *talking* in their own language, people like to hear things in a way they are most comfortable. The way they are used to. The way they can most easily relate to as if that makes it more real. So I will try to tell this story in that way.

And I will tell this story in first person.
I not *he. Me* not *him. Mine* not *his.*
In a neurotypical way.
I will try—
To tell my story in their language, in your language.

I am Jason Blake.

And this is what someone would say, if they looked at me but could only see and could only hear in their own language:

That kid is weird (he's in SPED, you know). He blinks his eyes, sometimes one at a time. Sometimes both together. They open and close, open and close, letting the light in, shutting it out. The word blinks on and off.

And he flaps his hands, like when he is excited or just before he is going to say something, or when he is thinking. He does that the most when he's on the computer or reading a book.

Generate Questions

In third grade Jason Blake was **diagnosed** with ASD, autistic spectrum disorder (range of autistic illnesses). When letters are put together, they can mean so much, and they can mean nothing at all.

From third grade until this year, sixth grade, Jason had a one-on-one aide, who followed him around the school all day. You couldn't miss seeing her.

But the thing people see the most is his silence, because some kinds of silence are actually visible.

School doesn't always go very well. It is pretty much a matter of time before the first thing of the day will go wrong.

But today I've gotten far. It is already third period. Mrs. Hawthorne is absent and so we are going to the library instead of art class. This is a good sign.

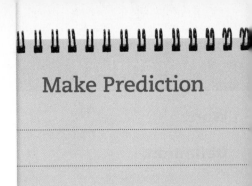

Make Prediction

Anything But Typical—Part One

Word:

Definition:

....

....

....

....

....

Word:

Definition:

....

....

....

....

There are computers in the library. And books. Keyboards and screens and desks that are built inside little compartments so you don't have to look at the person sitting next to you. And they can't look at me.

When we get into the library, somebody is already sitting in my seat, at my computer. At the one I want. Now I can't breathe.

"Jason, this one is free," the lady says. She puts her hands on my shoulders.

I know from experience that she is trying to help me, but it doesn't. I can feel her weight on my shoulders like metal cutting my body right off my head. This is not a good thing.

I know the right words to use.

I am okay just as I am.

"I am okay just as I am," I say, and I take a step forward. I want the librarian to take her hands off my shoulders.

The person at the computer turns around to the sound of my voice. It is a girl.

"I was here first, Miss Leno," the girl says.
Miss Leno is the librarian's name.
"Jason, here," Miss Leno is saying. "Sit here. You can use this computer."

Generate Questions

....

....

....

....

....

....

But I can't use that computer. I don't want to. I can't. My breathing is too loud inside my ears. I stiffen my body, **solidify** my weight, so she can't move me with her hands. You'd be surprised at how quickly people will try to move you with their hands when they don't get what they want with their words.

"Jason, hold still. There's no need to get so upset. There are plenty of other computers."

Miss Leno is trying to shift my weight off my feet, and she's trying to pretend she's not, as if she's just walking with me, instead of pushing me, which is what she is doing.

"Jason, please." But she doesn't mean *please*. There is no *please* in anything Miss Leno is asking. She is pulling me.

I feel off balance, like I am going to fall. I need to shift my weight back and forth, back and forth, rock to **stabilize** myself. I can feel my chance to use my computer getting further and further away from me. There isn't even enough time left in the period. I might not get to log on at all, even if this girl does get up. A hundred little pieces threaten to come apart.

"Jason, please, calm down. Calm down." Miss Leno's voice sounds like a Xerox machine.

Sometimes there is nothing to hold me together.

Verify Prediction

◯ CORRECT

◯ INCORRECT

Summarize

....

....

....

....

....

Vocabulary Review

Sentence When I freeze water, it will   and become ice.

Sentence I   chocolate to vanilla ice cream.

Sentence I started to fall on the ice, but my friend was there to
                  me.

Sentence When I was sick I went to the doctor, and she   me with
             the flu.

	Active Participation	Interactive Reader	Critical Thinking Application	Week 2 Total
TOTAL POINTS FOR WEEK 2				

Anything
But Typical

PART
TWO

By Nora Raleigh Baskin

Build Background

13

There are some writers who know things and post them on the Internet so other writers can learn them. Some of them say that there are only seven plots in the whole world:

Man vs nature.
Man vs man.
Man vs environment.
Man vs machine.
Man vs the supernatural.
Man vs self.
Man vs religion.

It could be a woman, too, but they just say "man" in order to make it easier for themselves. Because they all seem to be able to understand it, because they are only speaking in their own language. In an NT language.

But I can do that too.
When I try.
Very hard.
It means man or woman vs nature.
Man or woman vs man or woman.
    And so on.

Other writers say there are only three plots: happy ending, unhappy ending, and literary plot (that's the kind of ending that is uncertain). There is a whole book called *Twenty Master Plots,* which I happen to own. And another author wrote that he thought there were thirty-nine plots.

But really, if you ask me, there is only one kind of plot.
    One.

Generate Questions

Stuff happens.

That's it.

This is what happens next:

"C'mon, Maggie, get up. Give him that computer. You're not even doing anything."

Now Aaron Miller is standing behind me.

I have known Aaron Miller since kindergarten, from back when I was the same as everyone else. Nobody was very good at anything back then, and a lot of kids did weird things and didn't know enough to hide them. Charlie Karl wet his pants seven times that year. Chelsea Grey got caught sneaking into the cubbies and stealing the meat out of all the sandwiches she could find. Liza Duchamps picked her nose and ate it during circle time. Now that same girl is running for sixth-grade class president.

Aaron Miller was my friend in kindergarten. I'd like to say he still is, but by definition I can't. He hasn't come to my house in five years. He hasn't invited me to his birthday party since second grade. But he is always nice to me, and when I sit at his table at lunch, he will talk to me.

"What is it your **business?**" the girl, Maggie, says, but she stops her typing and looks at Aaron.

"Everything is my business, Maggie," Aaron says. "And you're just being **stubborn.** You're being mean."

Maggie says, "I'm not mean." She immediately signs off and closes the window she has open on the screen.

Word:

Definition:

Word:

Definition:

"All yours, Jay-Man," Aaron says.

The sooner you can begin something, the sooner it is done.

I am logging in.

The Storyboard home page rolls on to the screen, bit by bit, from the top down.

Now all I need to do is type in my screen name and password.

There are only twenty-two minutes left in this period, and I need to see if I got a response to my last posting.

One of the two responses to my story is from someone who calls themselves Nique79, which I think might be like Nick or even Nickie, but people like to spell things differently online.

Nique79 writes, `Great story. Keep writing.`

The second comment is from PhoenixBird, but I decided to wait until I get home from school to open it.

"Are you going to read your e-mails now?" Jeremy is asking me.

The best thing about Jeremy is that I don't ever have to answer him, not with words anyway. And I don't ever have to look him in the face. He likes to talk to me while he is watching TV or reading one of his comic books or biting his nails, which is what he is doing right now. He is very serious about biting his

Generate Questions

nails. My mom is always telling him to stop, so Jeremy doesn't ever do it when she can see him. That is one thing I really **admire** about my little brother.

I click on my second response, the one from PhoenixBird, the one I was saving until I got home.

I feel I could have written your story. It is so beautiful. I have to go to cheerleading practice but I can't wait for your next story.

I read it again. Sometimes the same words and letters can have different meanings, so you have to be careful.

"Why are you so quiet, Jason?"

Jeremy doesn't mean *quiet.* I am always quiet. He means **still.**

I am still.

I am completely still and I know it.

I read the comment one more time.

Because something tells me—

That this note is from a girl. There are some boy cheerleaders, but I don't think a boy would admit that.

So I think PhoenixBird is a girl.

So I think a girl has just said something nice to me.

Verify Prediction

○ CORRECT

○ INCORRECT

Summarize

Vocabulary Review

Word 1

Sentence

Word 2

Sentence

Word 3

Sentence

Word 4

Sentence

	Active Participation	Interactive Reader	Critical Thinking Application	Week 3 Total
TOTAL POINTS FOR WEEK 3				

Shakespeare and the Black Death

By Troy Markham

Build Background

Have you heard of a writer named William Shakespeare? His famous plays are sometimes funny, sometimes serious, and many times very sad. This is the story of a possible reason so many of his plays are just plain depressing.

During the bubonic **plague** in the sixteenth century, all of England lived in fear. The plague first struck two hundred years earlier, and it kept coming back. It became known as "the Black Death." Millions of people got sick and died. When Shakespeare was writing his most famous plays, the Black Death was terrorizing people all over Europe.

The plague was spread by the bites of fleas. The fleas lived on rats. England was filled with rats. The rats lived everywhere. This allowed the plague to spread quickly. A flea would bite a sick person. Then the flea would bite a healthy person. Then the healthy person would become sick too.

The times were dark. The plague felt like a huge gray shadow that covered everyone. It made people afraid because no one was safe from it.

Generate Questions

Shakespeare and the Black Death

Even children played games and sang songs about the plague. One song is "Ring Around the Rosie." The song is about the **symptoms** of the plague. Those include a rosy rash that is shaped like a ring. "A pocketful of posies" refers to flowers and herbs people carried in their pockets to keep the smell of the plague away.

Throughout Shakespeare's life, the plague struck again and again. It was worst in London. Thousands of people died there in one year alone. Often the theaters in London closed because of the plague. People stayed home or moved to the country, hoping they would not get the disease.

Even doctors were not safe. Of course they had to treat the sick people. That was risky for them. Most doctors wore masks and protective clothing, but sometimes even that was not enough.

Sickness was misery, and Shakespeare knew it. A person with the plague experienced intense pain and developed a high fever. The person would cough and become delirious. Finally, the person would become extremely tired. Once he or she fell asleep, their body would just give up, and death often followed. A person might die after only two or three days.

Word:

Definition:

....

....

....

Word:

Definition:

....

....

....

It is no wonder that Shakespeare wrote many plays about death. The plague struck Shakespeare's family many times when he was a child. Three sisters caught the plague and died. Plague killed many of the children who lived around him. He was lucky to survive, yet his fears haunted him. Like everyone else, Shakespeare could not escape the Black Death's grasp.

Finally the plague made its deepest cut. Shakespeare's son, Hamnet, became very ill. Shakespeare's nightmare had come true. Doctors did everything they could to save him. It was not enough. Hamnet died in 1596 when he was only eleven years old.

Generate Questions

....

....

....

....

....

Shakespeare and the Black Death

Before Hamnet's death, Shakespeare had written both comedies and tragedies. The comedies were called **farces.** They were filled with laughter, jokes, and silly plots. After his son's death, Shakespeare still wrote comedies and tragedies but there was a change. The comedies had a dark side. The tragedies were more personal. Terrible things happened to the characters. They spoke about death and worried about their **fate,** just as Shakespeare worried in real life.

Shakespeare's famous play *Hamlet* might have been inspired by his son. The main character's name, Hamlet, is similar to his son's name, Hamnet. The play is about murder, revenge, and death. Hamlet is worried and sad. In another play, *King John,* a mother who has just lost a child says, "Grief fills the room of my absent child."

Maybe writing helped Shakespeare express his sadness. All the feelings inside him could come out through his work. Maybe he wanted to show others how he felt. Did he feel relief by making his audience feel grief, too?

Shakespeare died at age fifty-two. Did the plague kill him? Most experts think not. We don't know, but we do know that Shakespeare's plays are among the greatest ever written. The terrible times he lived through may have helped him create characters we can still identify with to this day.

Verify Prediction

○ CORRECT

○ INCORRECT

Summarize

....

....

....

....

....

Vocabulary Review

Word 1

Definition

Word 2

Definition

Word 3

Definition

Word 4

Definition

	Active Participation	Interactive Reader	Critical Thinking Application	Week 4 Total
TOTAL POINTS FOR WEEK 4				

Shakespeare and the Black Death

● FICTION
● NONFICTION

THE
HARLEM HELLFIGHTERS
Heroes of World War I

By Dennis Fertig

Build Background

Word:

....

Definition:

....

....

....

....

....

Word:

....

Definition:

....

....

....

....

....

....

American soldier Horace Pippin had fought for months in the trenches of World War I. He was part of the 369th Infantry Regiment, and he knew about fear. Some fear was directed at the rats, diseases, and dead rotting bodies often found in the trenches. The bigger fear was of enemy soldiers and artillery.

Pippin crawled through the mud of no-man's-land. That was the dangerous ground between the American and German trenches. He didn't give into fear. He focused on his purpose. He had to kill a German **sniper** who had been shooting American soldiers. On this hot, wet night in August 1918, Pippin would stop that sniper, no matter what.

World War I began in 1914. It was a brutal war. Germany and its allies were on one side. Great Britain, France, and their allies were on the other. Millions of soldiers had been killed. Millions more were wounded. Yet neither side could win. America would change that. It entered the war in 1917. Americans joined the British and French.

In the summer of 1918, American soldiers made a difference. They helped Britain and France get closer to defeating Germany. The American soldiers in the 369th Infantry were part of the reason. They were highly successful in battle. That surprised some people. But why?

Generate Questions

....

....

....

....

....

Before America entered the war, the 369th Infantry was a volunteer unit in New York City. It was composed of African American soldiers. In those days, the US Armed Forces were segregated. Worse than that, many white people believed that African American soldiers couldn't fight. They thought African American soldiers should serve only as laborers far from battles.

The citizens who started the new regiment knew about that **prejudice.** They were determined to show that it was wrong. First, they had to recruit and train men to be soldiers. Many recruits came from Harlem, a large African American area in New York City. The regiment had few uniforms and rifles. Recruits trained in regular clothes. They did their drills with broomsticks instead of rifles.

Pippin was one of those recruits. His dream was to be an artist. Now patriotism came first. Like many young men, he wanted to help win the war. Yet when Pippin joined, no one was sure an African American regiment would be allowed to fight.

The Harlem Hellfighters: Heroes of World War I

When the 369th received real training, some of it was in South Carolina. Sadly many white people there had deep prejudices against African Americans. African American soldiers stationed there were often attacked. Facing that kind of danger made the men of the 369th learn to protect each other. This made them a stronger unit. They risked their lives for each other before they even went to war.

Pippin's unit arrived in France in early 1918. They were among the first American troops in Europe. Yet it looked like America's prejudice against its African American soldiers would keep them from fighting. But things changed quickly. First, the Germans were preparing a big attack. They had to end the war before millions of American soldiers arrived. That meant Britain and France would immediately need more soldiers.

Second, France's army already had many black African soldiers. Because the French needed fresh troops, the U.S. Army did something unusual. It allowed the 369th to temporarily become part of the French army. By spring 1918, while most of the American army prepared for war, the 369th was already fighting in bloody trenches.

From the start, the 369th Infantry showed fierceness in battle. The Germans saw it. After a few **intense** fights, German soldiers had a nickname for the 369th—the Hellfighters!

Generate Questions

Pippin crawled farther into no-man's-land. He spotted the tree where the sniper hid. It was a rainy dawn. Pippin might soon be visible to the enemy. Still he waited. Around noon, Pippin noticed leaves moving in the tree. He aimed and fired. In seconds, a rifle and a dead German soldier fell to the ground. Pippin had stopped the sniper!

Just weeks later, a magazine article told the story about the brave 369th Infantry. Millions of Americans read it. This article helped people understand that good soldiers come in all colors.

The war ended in November 1918. Germany was defeated. The Hellfighters' record was incredible. The unit was in battle for 191 days, the longest of any American unit. It never lost any ground in that time. Many men received medals from the United States and France. Yet the 389th paid the price for bravery. More than 1,500 Hellfighters were killed or wounded. That was the largest number of any American regiment in World War I.

The Hellfighters' **triumphs** proved that African Americans were excellent soldiers. However, the unit's heroes still faced prejudice back in America.

Pippin made it home but with a wound that permanently damaged his right arm. He still fulfilled his dream. He became a respected artist. Bad arm or not, Pippin knew he could succeed. After all, he had already fought through a war and won.

Verify Prediction

◯ CORRECT

◯ INCORRECT

Summarize

....

....

....

....

....

Sentence The coach had many _____ against tough teams.

Sentence The _____ hid behind the wall and took aim at the victim.

Sentence The kids at my school have _____ toward kids at another school because they wear uniforms.

Sentence The smell of the rotting apple was _____ .

	Active Participation	Interactive Reader	Critical Thinking Application	Week 5 Total
TOTAL POINTS FOR WEEK 5				

The Harlem Hellfighters: Heroes of World War I

BEHIND THE MASK:

The Real Story of King Tut

By Hilary Mac Austin

Build Background

31

Word:
....

Definition:
....

....

....

....

Word:
....

Definition:
....

....

....

....

Tutankhamen is one of the most famous pharaohs in Egyptian history. But Tut's fame does not come from a long and successful **reign.** In fact, even though he is famous, not very much is known about him. What we do know began with a discovery in 1922.

It was early morning on November 4. A boy in the Valley of the Kings dug a hole in the sand. He was a water carrier for a team of archaeologists. He wanted a place to keep the water jar cool. As he dug his hole, he hit something hard. He had discovered a step. Luckily he told the lead archeologist, Howard Carter.

When Howard Carter was only seventeen, he went to Egypt. It was in the 1890s. He'd had a job with another team of archaeologists. He drew pictures. When the team found a statue, he drew it. When they found writing, he drew that. For more than six years, that was his job. Then, Carter began to lead teams himself. Now he was about to make the biggest discovery of his life.

Generate Questions

....

....

....

....

Behind the Mask: The Real Story of King Tut

Carter began digging at the spot the water carrier showed him. He dug carefully, as always. It took time, but it was worth it. He uncovered a **tomb.**

At that time most ancient Egyptian tombs had already been found. They had also been robbed. Not this one. Robbers had invaded the tomb twice. But they had found only the outer room. On November 26, Carter found a second doorway. This one was still sealed. Carter made a very small hole in the door. He held up a candle and looked into the tomb.

The inner rooms were untouched. No one had been inside for three thousand years! They were full of gold, jewels, statues, and paintings. They also held everything anyone would need to be happy in the afterlife. There were board games, a razor, underclothes, food, and wine.

Most important, Carter found the mummy of a young man. Gold jewelry lay on the mummy. A beautiful gold mask covered his head. He was surrounded by gold.

No one had ever found such a rich tomb. The whole world was amazed. People could not stop talking about the young king. Who was he? Why had no one heard of him?

The basic details of Tutankhamen's life can be told in a few sentences. He was born around 1336 B.C. He became pharaoh when he was only eight or nine. He was raised to be a **warrior** like all pharaohs, but he died when he was in his late teens. Because he died young, his royal tomb was not finished. Instead he was buried in the small tomb in the Valley of the Kings. Many years later, the tomb of Ramses VI was built above Tut's tomb. When Ramses's tomb was built, tons of stone chips fell over the entrance of Tut's tomb. King Tut disappeared until Howard Carter found him.

However, there is more to Tut's story. **Modern** science has found information Carter could not have imagined. It has led to a very real picture of the young king.

Scientists made X-rays of the mummy in 1968. They thought they saw something in this skull. They could not be sure. But they thought he might have been hit on the head. He might have been murdered.

Generate Questions

Behind the Mask: The Real Story of King Tut

Then, in 2005, the Egyptian government and *National Geographic* magazine decided to scan Tut's mummy. The scan created 1,700 digital X-ray images of the body. Three teams of scientists then looked at the details of the head. They created three pictures of what Tutankhamen probably looked like when he was alive. They all looked very much alike. Imagine what Howard Carter would have felt if he saw them!

When he died, Tut was about five feet and six inches tall. The shape of his head was quite long. He had a slight build and had led a healthy life. He had no cavities.

So how did he die so young? The 2005 scan proved that Tut had *not* been murdered—at least, not by a blow to the head. The scan showed a badly broken leg. Now some people believe the young king broke his leg, and an infection or blood clot caused his death. Others are not so sure. They say the leg may have been broken by Howard Carter when he tried to remove the mummy from the coffin. Tut's death is still a mystery.

Maybe someday science will find a way to uncover more secrets of the life and death of the famous boy king of Egypt. Or maybe another fabulous tomb may be uncovered by a boy digging a hole for a water jug in the Valley of the Kings.

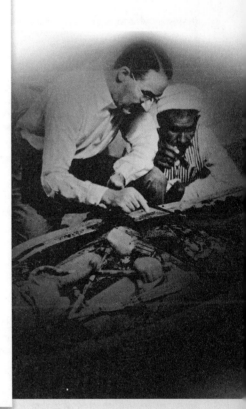

Summarize

....

....

....

....

....

Vocabulary Review

Word 1

Sentence

Word 2

Sentence

Word 3

Sentence

Word 4

Sentence

	Active Participation	Interactive Reader	Critical Thinking Application	Week 6 Total
TOTAL POINTS FOR WEEK 6				

Behind the Mask: The Real Story of King Tut

THE DANCE OF
KNiVES AND FiRE

By Kathleen Thompson

Build Background

It was 1946, one year after World War II ended. Golden Gate Park was filled with visitors. Children ran across the huge green lawns. Families sat under the trees. Tourists took pictures. They looked happily at the park's beauty. Everyone was enjoying a beautiful day in San Francisco.

In one part of the park, a special group of visitors was hard at work. They were practicing their acts for the Shriners Convention. One young woman was twirling a **baton.** It had light bulbs at both ends. It made a circle of light as it spun. A man from India named Abe Sing was eating fire. It was a strange trick with a special kind of fire. Near them, a young man was doing a kind of standing dance with a long, sharp knife. It was a traditional dance from Samoa. It was very difficult and dangerous. The man's name was Freddie Letuli, and he was about to invent one of the most remarkable dances in the world.

Generate Questions

The Dance of Knives and Fire

Freddie Letuli was born Uluao Letuli Misilagi in 1919. He was from the Samoan Islands in the Pacific Ocean. Even as a boy, Letuli loved to dance. He learned the **traditional** dances of Samoa, but he also learned popular dances. When he was fifteen years old, he ordered tap shoes from the *Sears* catalog. The shoes came with an instruction booklet written by movie star Fred Astaire. Astaire was one of the greatest tap dancers in history. Everyone knew him from his movies. Letuli practiced tap dancing so much that people started calling him Freddie. The name stuck.

Letuli decided to spend his life dancing. He went to the United States and began getting jobs as an entertainer. He was twenty-seven years old when he got his big idea. "I stared at the fire-eater, then the baton twirler. The baton twirler, then the fire-eater. And just like that, I had an idea to add 'sizzle' to my knife dance," he said. He borrowed some white gas from the fire-eater. Then he soaked a cloth with it and wrapped the cloth around his knife. The Fire Knife Dance was born.

Make Prediction

15   30 km

Mercator Projection

Safotu   Fagamalo
Asau
lelima   Mt. Silisili   Pu'apu'a
             1858 m
             ▲ 6095 ft
Savai'i   Tuasivi
Sala'ilua   Salelologa
Taga   Apolima Strait
            Apolima
            Manono   Upol
         Falelatai
            Matautu   14°

PACIFIC   Bay   Nu'utele
                Nu'ulua

Letuli went on to perform his new dance all over the United States and Europe. He was a huge success. He appeared in several Hollywood movies. Letuli often appeared on the television series *Adventures in Paradise.* Then his country called him home. The governor of the **territory** asked him to serve in the Department of Education. He was selected to serve in the village senate in 1977. Then in 1993 he was elected to the Samoan Senate. Letuli was one of the most important men in American Samoa.

All this time, however, Letuli also taught the Fire Knife Dance to young people. It quickly became popular. Soon, hundreds of young men performed the dance. They added new moves and improved the techniques. Letuli **promoted** them as they dazzled tourists and other Samoans. He helped organize the first World Fire Knife Competition, held in 2003. He died the same year. Feddie Letuli had changed Samoan tradition forever.

Generate Questions

The Dance of Knives and Fire

Before Freddie Letuli, the knife dance was performed without fire, but it was already fierce. It began hundreds of years ago as a way for warriors to get ready to fight. The men lined up in rows and gestured with their long knives. Later, individual men began performing with the long knives for tourists. Now the Fire Knife Dance has become one of the things American Samoa is most famous for. It is performed at luaus almost as frequently as the hula. There are Fire Knife competitions in many places around the Pacific.

There are Fire Knife dancers in other parts of the world. A young American boy named Preston Weber saw the dance at a restaurant in Fort Lauderdale, Florida. He taught himself how to do it. Then he began performing around the area. He performs and competes under the name "Chief Malosi" and designs his own moves. In 2010, he was invited to compete, at the age of eleven, in the World Fire Knife Competition in Hawaii.

Uluao Letuli Misilagi was proud of the dance he helped create on that beautiful day in San Francisco. He was always happy to give credit to fire-eater Abe Sing. Now, if only we knew the name of the baton twirler!

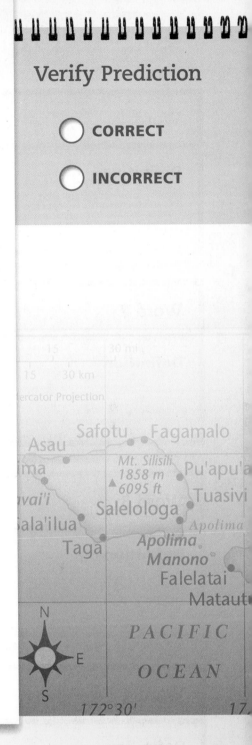

Verify Prediction

○ CORRECT

○ INCORRECT

Summarize

....

....

....

....

....

Vocabulary Review

Word 1

Definition

Word 2

Definition

Word 3

Definition

Word 4

Definition

TOTAL POINTS FOR WEEK 7	Active Participation	Interactive Reader	Critical Thinking Application	Week 7 Total

The Dance of Knives and Fire

Listening for Crickets

By David Gifaldi   **Part One**

● **FICTION**
● **NONFICTION**

Build Background

One of my best dreams ever. A flying dream. Me, Jake Wasniewski, with wings like a megabat, a flying fox. Powerful wings. A single stroke shoots me into an **updraft,** my stomach racing to keep up. Farms and rivers slide by. Up ahead, a city of glass, shining like a treasure in the sun. Then . . . voices. My bat ears twitch. *Huh?*

They're at it again. Smack in the middle of my flying dream. I check the clock on the nightstand, the green numbers ghosting 11:35. The back-and-forth words coming from the kitchen get louder, sharper.

Wish our house had an upstairs like Luke's.

Wish I had a remote control that could mute anything.

"Jake," Cassie **murmurs.**

"It's okay," I say, reaching to flick on the lamp.

Cassie squints even though the yellow light is dim. She listens to the harsh-sounding words, then rolls out of bed, Thumper tucked safely under one arm.

Scampering around to the bed's other side, she squeezes between mattress and wall, and pushes, grunts. The bed moans, then gives in to be scraped across the floor. Cassie pushes—grunts—until the mattress bumps the nightstand.

Generate Questions

"You can't be moving your bed right up to mine," I've had to tell her more than once. "See that nightstand there? . . . That's the limit. That's the boundary. That whole strip there is poison. It's bad enough we have to share the same room, bad enough you get scared. A guy needs his privacy."

She smiles over at me, that goofy seven-year-old grin of hers, then bounds up onto the mattress, slithers under the sheet, moves Thumper up top for air, and sighs. "You can turn the light off now."

"Oh, can I?" I say, a little mad at the bossy sound of her voice, as if a soon-to-be second grader could ever tell a soon-to-be fifth grader what to do.

Mom and Dad are flinging spears at each other. *I'm selfish? Look who's talking. Me? Don't make me laugh! You don't have a clue, do you?* . . .

"Okay, Jake," Cassie says through the new dark.

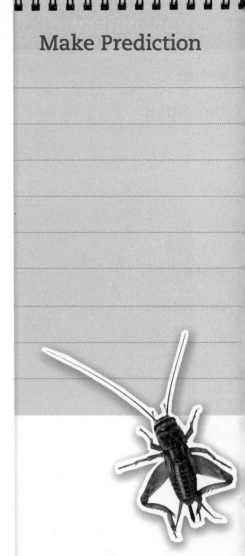

Make Prediction

That means it's time for another story. Sometimes I wish I hadn't started this whole story thing. As if telling stories to your little sister could ever cover up arguing.

"You'd better be listening," I say, "because I'm starting right now and the last time you didn't hear the beginning because you were listening to something else. You hear?"

"Uh-huh."

Suddenly the back-and-forth spears stop. The front door slamming—so hard the whole house jumps, including my ears. Lights swing past the window as the car backs onto the street. I wait until I can't hear the engine anymore.

"Jake?"

"Dang it, Cassie. Hold your horses."

I cross my hands behind my head, slide my feet beneath the sheet to find some fresh cool. At least I won't have to talk loud.

"Once," I begin. "Once there was a baby dragon named Smoke. A girl dragon. And she had a brother dragon named Bonfire. And the two liked to stomp over the world and play all the latest dragon games . . . like . . ."

"Like what?" Cassie says, unable to stop herself. There's real interest in her voice, and I can tell she's glad too that the shouting has stopped.

"I'm thinking," I say.

Generate Questions

I draw circles with my toes under the sheet and go on, telling whatever comes to mind, about Smoke and Bonfire, about their life in a tiny cave on the side of a mountain, how the two are learning to fly, how Bonfire did his first loop-de-loop today, how Smoke got so excited she **torched** one of the trees outside the cave.

I keep talking until Cassie's even breathing lets me know she's asleep. I listen hard for **wheezing,** but her air sounds clear. Then Mom taps at the door and steps in, a strip of living-room light cutting across my bed.

"You kids okay?"

I don't say anything.

She moves to our beds, checks Cassie, sees the bed has been moved again.

"Yeah," I answer.

I turn over just as she leans down to kiss me, turn quickly so I won't have to see if she's been crying.

"Good night, then," she whispers.

"'Night," I say into my pillow, thinking of where I want the new dragon story to go . . . how next time maybe Smoke and Bonfire will leave their tiny cave for a bigger and better one . . . one with room after room after room, high up on the tallest mountain, where the air is so clean you can breathe it all the way down to your toes and not wheeze or cough.

The clock shows 12:00. Midnight. I close my eyes and reach for my wings.

Summarize

....

....

....

....

....

Vocabulary Review

Sentence   The lightning   the forest and made it burn.

Sentence   The little girl   when she talks because she is so shy.

Sentence   The eagle used the   to climb high in the sky.

Sentence   The soccer player had a lot of   after she ran the field.

	Active Participation	Interactive Reader	Critical Thinking Application	Week 8 Total
TOTAL POINTS FOR WEEK 8				

Listening for *Crickets*

Part Two

By David Gifaldi

● FICTION
● NONFICTION

Build Background

49

Generate Questions

Everything'll be all right. But it never gets right. Not really. Just a little right here and a little right there. And in between are the wrongs: the yelling and swear words and slamming doors.

I wake up with an idea. A cave. Like Smoke and Bonfire's. Cassie and I spend the whole morning building it.

"It'll be a place only we know about," I say. "You can't tell Mom or Dad or anyone. You hear?"

I use Dad's **pruning** saw and Mom's rose snippers to cut. I'm like a surgeon, called in special for the job. I have to cut out the hedge's insides without disturbing the outside walls and ceiling.

Now that I've got a good start, I call Cassie. She grunts, holding aside the two big leafy limbs that form the outermost layer, and slips in to where I am.

We saw and snip till we end up with a little cave room. Then we find stones for seats and move them in. There's just enough room for us both, our knees nearly touching. The sun fights its way through the leaves, forming yellow polka dots on our skin and clothes.

"Feels like a nest," Cassie says.

"Hey, it does," I say. "That's what we'll call it. Dragon's Nest."

"Do dragons have nests?"

"I don't know. They might. But it's a good name, don't you think?"

She nods.

"But the important thing is that now you have a place to go in case you get scared. And me too. And if something happens, and we can't find each other, we'll know where the other person is."

"Won't Dad be mad if he finds out?"

"He's not *finding* out!" I say. "Unless you tell. . . . Now go back outside and we'll test it."

When she's out, I tell her to walk all the way to the shed.

"Can you see me?"

"No! I mean, I know where you are 'cause of the stick pile. But you're right . . . there's too many leaves."

"Told you," I say as I come out. "I couldn't see you either, 'cept right at the end. Now we have got to **ditch** the evidence."

I get a trash bag from the shed. We put in all the branches and sticks and drag the bag around to Mrs. Pittmon's. There's already a bunch of bags in the corner of the yard, so I'm sure she won't mind.

We go back to Dragon's Nest and toss a few sticks we missed into the hedge. "Now we have to cross our hearts," I say. "And promise not to tell and never to let anyone see us going in or coming out."

Make Prediction

We sign crosses. I make sure to put the saw and snippers back exactly like they were. When we go inside for a drink, Mom's cleaning out the kitchen cabinet drawers. She's got silverware and junk piled all over. "I figured the next time I cleaned these drawers we'd be moving to a house with a *real* kitchen," she says. "You guys want a sandwich for lunch?"

"Mashed potatoes!" Cassie says.

"Not for lunch," Mom says. She grabs the peanut butter and jam from the fridge. "What've you been up to all this time, anyway?"

I give Cassie a look. "Just playing," I say.

That night, Cassie's putting down paper towels for napkins and I'm counting out forks and spoons when Dad comes in the back door. He winks at me, one hand behind his back, then clears his throat to get Mom to turn his way. "Is this the **residence** of Roxanne Wasniewski?" he says, bowing at the waist.

Mom squints, grins. "You look like the cat who swallowed the canary. What's eating you?"

It's the most they've said to each other in two days.

Mom's shoulders drop, and a smile sneaks over her face. That's when Dad brings his hand from behind his back and offers a skinny bouquet of flowers with the Safeway sticker still on the green plastic wrapping.

Generate Questions

Mom brings the bouquet up to her nose. "Well," she says, her eyes all shiny. "Well."

Cassie gives a tug on my shirt. I meet her smile with a **confident** nod, like I knew all along that Dad and Mom would make up.

After supper the four of us play Monopoly. We squeeze around the board, which is on the floor between the TV and the sofa. It's the first game we've played together in a long time. Mom's money pile is the biggest.

Cassie's in charge of the Cheetos. She counts out four whenever anyone passes GO.

"Jake, why don't you and Cassie get us some pop," Mom says after a while.

When I get back to the game, Dad's handing over another stack of money to Mom.

"You're rich, Mommy," Cassie says.

Mom counts the new bills and puts them in her bank. "I feel lucky," she says.

I take the dice and let Cassie blow Cheetos breath over them. Then I shake them hard in my hands, feeling lucky too.

Verify Prediction

○ CORRECT

○ INCORRECT

Summarize

Vocabulary Review

Word 1
Sentence

Word 2
Sentence

Word 3
Sentence

Word 4
Sentence

	Active Participation	Interactive Reader	Critical Thinking Application	Week 9 Total
TOTAL POINTS FOR WEEK 9				

Listening for Crickets

By David Gifaldi

Part Three

● FICTION
● NONFICTION

Build Background

55

Word:
....

Definition:
....

....

....

....

Word:
....

Definition:
....

....

....

Cassie's been strapped into her Barbie backpack since she got dressed. "Come on, Jake, we'll be late!"

I'm a little worried about seeing everyone after so long. A lot can happen over the summer. You never know if your buddy in June still wants to be your friend in September.

School is **mobbed** when we get there. Parents and kids crowd the office window, checking the class lists.

I make sure Cassie finds one of her friends, then head for the fifth-grade **wing.**

When the bell rings we file inside. The desk with my name is in the back, in a group of six, with Andy, Molly, Devon, Joanna, and a new girl named Michelle.

The teacher, Mr. Wyatt, spends all morning talking about how great a year we're going to have if we follow all the rules. Problem is, there are about a hundred rules.

Mr. Wyatt is new to the school. He must think we're all smart. After lunch he wants everyone to write about themselves. "At least a page," he says, "but you'll probably end up writing much more than that."

I hear a few gulps, including mine.

"I love to write," Michelle says. "Don't you?"

Generate Questions

....

....

....

....

She's looking at me, looking across our two desks. She asked me a question, and now she's waiting for an answer. I shrug. Like I don't understand. Like I can't speak the language. Maybe she'll think I'm one of the Spanish- or Russian-speaking kids.

My stomach is in one big knot as I get out a sheet of paper. It takes me a long time to get the heading right, copying from the sample on the overhead.

Mr. Wyatt is walking around the room, commenting on everybody's work. I feel him stop behind me. He'll probably tell me I'm slow as molasses . . . slow as a tortoise . . . a snail. I've heard them all before.

He's still standing there, not saying anything as I move the pencil. I lift my finger from the pencil and shake my hand like it hurts. Maybe he'll think I've got a sprain or a broken finger. He just waits. I start from where I left off.

"You have nice handwriting, Jake."

The suddenness of his voice makes me jump. I wait for the rest: *Maybe you could speed it up a bit. Put it in second gear.* But it doesn't come. He moves on toward the front of the room and asks for everyone's attention.

"Some people are better at drawing than writing," he says. "If you want, instead of writing everything out, you can draw little snapshots of who you are. Snapshots of what's important to you . . . your family, pets, hopes. Stuff like that."

I look at Desiree across the way. She smiles, like she's as happy as I am to hear that we can draw instead of write. Austin too. All of us in the LEP class. It's like we all give a big sigh of relief, then start in on our drawings.

I fold my paper into fourths. On one side I draw me, Cassie, Mom, and Dad. On the other side I draw a flying fox, Nina and Otto on their cushions, Mrs. Pittmon's wheelchair, and the Vista Park Pool. Michelle says I'm a good drawer. When she's done writing, she draws a dog in the margin of her paper. "I'm not very good," she says.

The best thing about the first day is that the LEP kids get to go to Mrs. Maw's for a Welcome Back party.

Tyler, a college student and Mrs. Maw's new assistant, is the tallest teacher I've ever seen. He gives me a thumbs-up and tells me to help myself to the juice and cookies.

I look around the room. Purple and yellow balloons hang from the ceiling. Everything looks shiny and new.

Mrs. Maw calls us over to the circular table and tells us about the school's new reading program. "Your teachers will be telling the rest of your classes about it sometime soon, but I wanted my kids to have a **sneak preview.**"

Generate Questions

She points to a shelf filled with books. The spine of each book has a colored circle taped to it. Some are green, some pink, some blue, and some orange.

"The program is called Everyone Reads. Each book in the school with a colored dot will be an E-R book. That means there's a computer test you can take whenever you finish a story. The tests show if you understand what you've read."

"What'll we get if we pass the test?"

"You'll probably find you're becoming a better reader," Tyler the Tall says.

"Plus, you earn points," Mrs. Maw says. "When you reach a certain number of points you'll earn special **privileges**. We might even celebrate from time to time as we progress—parties and that kind of thing. Of course, I understand that fifth graders are too old for parties."

"WHAT?"

"Not fair! No way can fourth graders get parties and we can't."

Mrs. Maw shrugs. "Well, then, parties it'll be, as long as you read more than you've ever read before."

Verify Prediction

◯ CORRECT

◯ INCORRECT

Summarize

_____

_____

_____

_____

Vocabulary Review

Word 1

Definition

Word 2

Definition

Word 3

Definition

Word 4

Definition

	Active Participation	Interactive Reader	Critical Thinking Application	Week 10 Total
TOTAL POINTS FOR WEEK 10				

FICTION
NONFICTION

The Curious Case of PHINEAS GAGE

By Troy Markham

Build Background

Word:
....

Definition:
....
....
....
....

Word:
....

Definition:
....
....
....
....

Have you ever struggled to **function** after you got something in your eye? A speck of dust blown by the wind can be irritating.

Imagine how painful having a large steel rod in your eye would be. This is what happened to Phineas Gage. The rod went through his eye and out the top of his head. You would think this probably killed him. But you would be wrong. It barely slowed him down.

It all started on a normal day in September 1848. Gage was working with a group of men. They were clearing land to build railroad tracks. Some of the men would drill holes into rock. His job was to follow them and pack the holes with gunpowder. A fuse would be lit, and the rock blasted away. Gage used a long iron rod to pack the gunpowder into the hole.

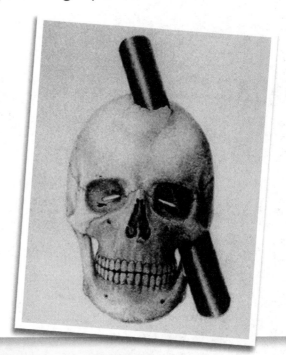

Generate Questions

....
....
....
....

Suddenly the gunpowder exploded in one hole. Gage had been using the iron bar to pack that hole. The bar shot up through his head. It blasted into his left cheek and traveled through his brain. It flew out the top of his head with such force that it landed several yards behind him. It was covered in blood and brain tissue.

Gage fell down, and those around him assumed he was dead. Amazingly, though, he sat back up and started asking for a doctor. He was even able to stand, walk, and climb into a cart, which took him home.

Back at home, the doctor bandaged his cheek and head. The hole through Gage's head was large. As the doctor worked to bandage it, he thought it was not likely that Gage would live.

But Gage continued to surprise everyone. He seemed remarkably healthy for a man with a huge hole in his head. But he had lost a lot of blood, too. His wound became infected, and he fell into a **coma.** His family assumed he was going to die. They bought a coffin and prepared for his funeral.

Word: ....

Definition: ....

....

....

....

Word: ....

Definition: ....

....

....

....

Then Gage did another amazing thing. He woke up from the coma. He began to walk and talk. He acted very much *not* like a man who was missing a lot of his brain. In fact, he seemed like a normal, healthy person. His doctor wrote an **account** of his injury and recovery. He sent the account to a medical journal. Other doctors did not believe it. Only after another doctor examined him did the journal publish the story.

In the meantime, Gage did not seem concerned with the accident. He had lost vision in one eye the bar had traveled through. But he was otherwise not obviously affected.

Gage walked around, talked to people, and behaved normally. His memory was good, and he was able to think and reason. He even asked to keep the iron bar. He began using it as a walking stick. He carried the iron bar with him for the rest of his life.

However, slowly those around him realized something was different. Losing a large part of his brain did not seem to affect his physical activities. But Gage had been changed. His behavior was different.

He seemed much more **irritable** and lost his temper easily. He could not focus on his work. The people who knew him said he seemed to have a completely different personality.

Generate Questions

....

....

....

....

....

The Curious Case of Phineas Gage

Before the accident, Gage had been a hard worker. He was well liked by the other workers and was trusted to make decisions. But when he returned to work after the accident, it was a different story. The other workers noted that he was often angry. He became lazy and would curse at others. He goofed off a lot and got into fights. He soon lost his job.

Because of this personality change, Gage's experience was helpful to scientists and doctors. They learned many things about how the brain functions. For example, we know that many parts of the brain are not used for movement or speech. These parts control emotions and behavior. These parts of Gage's brain were damaged. The rest of his brain was fine.

Gage traveled for several years as part of circus shows. People would pay to see his head injury and the metal bar that caused it. Twelve years after his accident, Gage's health began to decline. He started suffering from convulsions (an uncontrolled fit where muscles contract and relax) and soon died.

Several years later, scientists dug up his body to use for scientific investigations. The studies that were done on his brain helped create the field of brain science. This information helps save people's lives today.

Verify Prediction

○ CORRECT

○ INCORRECT

Summarize

....

....

....

....

....

Vocabulary Review

Sentence A calculator can   to make math easier.

Sentence Jack was   because he didn't get enough sleep.

Sentence The man was in a   for two days after his car accident.

Sentence Her   of her trip to China was exciting.

	Active Participation	Interactive Reader	Critical Thinking Application	Week 11 Total
TOTAL POINTS FOR WEEK 11				

The Curse of
The Hope Diamond

By Hilary Mac Austin

Build Background

Imagine a hot, dry night long, long ago. You are in India in a Hindu temple. Over in the corner is a huge stone statue of the goddess Siva. An enormous deep blue diamond decorates her forehead. Suddenly you hear a sound! A man is sneaking toward the statue. He climbs on the goddess and pries the gem from the stone. Before you can cry out, the man has run away.

The man thinks he has won a great prize. Little does he know that this gem is now cursed forever!

This is the beginning of a legend that is the Curse of the Hope Diamond. Now, curses aren't real, and the legend is make-believe, but the Hope Diamond is one of the most famous and fascinating gems in the world. It has been owned by kings, lords, gamblers, and **heiresses.** It has been cut down in size to be more beautiful and to look like a different stone.

The real story is almost as interesting as the legend. It probably started like this: One day in the middle of the 1600s, a miner in the Kullur mine in Golconda, India, found one of the biggest, rarest diamonds the world has ever seen. It was about the size of a walnut and was deep blue. It was 112.75 carats. (A carat is the way gems are measured. It is a measure of the mass of a stone, not its weight.)

Generate Questions

The Curse of the Hope Diamond

A local merchant sold the diamond to a Frenchman named Jean-Baptiste Tavernier. Tavernier went back to France, and in 1668 Louis XIV, the king of France, bought the diamond from him. Some say the curse started with Tavernier. One story even says he was killed by wild dogs! There is no evidence this ever happened, though. Tavernier did have some bad luck. He was in prison, his ship was sunk, and he was in a war. But he also became a nobleman and lived to be eighty-four years old. So maybe his luck wasn't too bad after all.

Louis XIV enjoyed his new diamond. He cut the gemstone, adding **facets** that made it sparkle more brilliantly. Now the stone was 67 carats, not 112. But it was more beautiful. It became part of the French crown jewels, and the king wore the gem on a ribbon around his neck. At this time the stone was called the French Blue.

The Curse of the Hope Diamond

The curse did not seem to affect Louis XIV or his great-grandson, the next king, Louis XV. But the king after that, Louis XVI, had *very* bad luck. He was **beheaded** during the French Revolution. This was probably not the curse, though. It was probably because he was a very bad king.

The French Revolution also meant the end of the stone known as the French Blue. The crown jewels were not guarded safely. Sometime in 1791 or 1792, the French Blue was stolen. No one has ever seen it again.

That is not the end of the story, however. A few years later a mysterious large blue diamond appeared in England. It was only 45.5 carats. People believe the thieves who stole the French Blue had cut it down to make it look different. This stone was sold to George IV, the king of England.

Next, the diamond was sold to a man named Henry Philip Hope. It is from this man that the Hope Diamond got its name. He bought the diamond in the 1830s, and it stayed in the Hope family for the next seventy years. Finally, in the late 1800s, the diamond was owned by Lord Francis Hope. He gambled too much, ruined his marriage, and needed money, so in 1901 he sold the diamond. Was he cursed by the diamond or by his gambling?

Generate Questions

Evalyn Walsh McLean loved mysterious stories. She was also very, very rich. In 1911, the jeweler Pierre Cartier wanted to sell her the Hope Diamond. He made up stories about a curse. This was the first time anyone had said the diamond was cursed.

At first, McLean didn't want the stone. She liked the stories, but she didn't like the stone's setting. Cartier didn't give up. He put the stone in a new setting. This cut the stone down to 45.52 carats, but it did convince McLean to buy the gem.

McLean wore the Hope Diamond all the time. She loved her jewel. She had a lot of bad luck. She lost most of her money because she spent too much. Her husband left her, and two of her children died. McLean did not blame this on any curse. She said, "Tragedies, for anyone who lives, are not **escapable.**"

The famous jeweler Harry Winston bought the diamond after McLean died. In 1958 he gave the diamond to its current owner, the Smithsonian Institution in Washington, DC. Now everyone can look at the most beautiful diamond in the world and not be afraid of being cursed! (Or can they?)

Verify Prediction

○ CORRECT

○ INCORRECT

Summarize

Vocabulary Review

Word 1

Sentence

Word 2

Sentence

Word 3

Sentence

Word 4

Sentence

	Active Participation	Interactive Reader	Critical Thinking Application	Week 12 Total
TOTAL POINTS FOR WEEK 12				

Creepy, Crawly Neighbors!

By Dennis Fertig

Build Background

Word:

Definition:

Word:

Definition:

When Diane Barger, her husband, and children moved into their house in Kansas, they knew it was filled with history. The oldest part was built in the 1800s, and lawman Wild Bill Hickok once lived there. Yet the family didn't know that more than history lurked in the house. Something else filled its roof, walls, and floors. In fact, five years passed before the Barger family discovered they weren't alone. They had housemates—lots of them. The Bargers were living with creatures that most people would find very frightening. They were poisonous brown recluse spiders!

Brown recluse spiders are usually a brown or yellow color. They have marks on their backs that look a bit like a violin. When the recluse is fully grown, its body is about a quarter of an inch long. Its legs spread out about an inch. That doesn't sound very big—until you see one!

All spiders are **predators.** To survive they must catch and eat living things such as insects or other spiders. One hunting tool many spider species have is **venom,** which they use to stun their prey. Only a few species have venom that can harm humans. The brown recluse spider is one, and it has a frightening reputation. Many people believe a single recluse bite can kill a human.

Generate Questions

Creepy, Crawly Neighbors!

Generally, people are calm around spiders. They understand that most species aren't usually threats. The eight-legged little critters keep down the populations of harmful insect pests that eat crops or damage houses.

A number of people are terrified of spiders. These people suffer from arachnophobia (an extreme fear of spiders). Their fear is often so strong they aren't able to kill spiders. Or, if they do, they must take great precautions. They wear gloves or use a long stick.

In the Barger family, one person had arachnophobia—Diane. During the first five years in the house, she would spot a spider now and then. Her quick response was to vacuum it up. She never wondered what kind of spider it was. Diane has a college degree in chemistry, but her fears blocked her normal scientific curiosity.

One day Diana saw a spider stuck in a glass jar. She didn't know it, but the spider's inability to escape was a sign that it was a recluse. Other species would have been able to walk up the glass.

Thirteen-year-old Brenna Barger, Diane's daughter, studied the spider. She announced it was a brown recluse. To be sure, the Bargers asked University of Kansas's entomology (the study of insects) department to take a look. Then the family knew for certain that Brenna was right. They also realized there had to be more recluses in the house.

Now the family paid attention to their housemates. They spent nights hunting recluses. Diane set out sticky glue boards on floors. The spiders walked onto them and didn't walk away. In just one week of trapping, the Bargers found one hundred spiders!

Richard Vetter heard about the Barger house. He was a spider expert at the University of California, Riverside. Soon he was in touch with Diane. He was happy to discover that the family had saved the bodies of the spiders they had rounded up. That meant if the Barger family was willing, they could begin a count of how many recluses lived in their house.

In a six-month period, the Bargers collected more than two thousand spiders! All were sent to Vetter. He knew recluses had to be a certain size before they had enough venom to harm humans. He discovered that four hundred of the dead spiders were big enough. Yet he wasn't surprised that no one in the family had been bitten.

Generate Questions

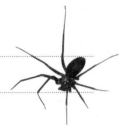

Creepy, Crawly Neighbors!

Vetter studies the dangers spiders **potentially** pose to humans. He studies reported recluse bites. His research shows that although recluses do bite people, there is usually little harm done. Some people get sick after they think a recluse has bitten them, but Vetter routinely finds that the illness comes from something else. In fact, many so-called recluse bites occur in places where recluses don't even live.

Yet the recluses did live—and still do—in the Barger house. The Bargers still live there, too. Over the years, the count of their little housemates has hit more than seven thousand! Yet the family still has no known bites. The spiders hide, so the Bargers rarely see them unless they actually hunt for them.

Some good things have happened because of the recluses. Diane's fear is under control. Brenna's interaction with spiders **confirmed** her love of living things in general. She will be a veterinarian soon. Diane's son Bradley once disliked spiders. Now he has an advanced college degree in medical entomology. He has studied how insects and spiders affect the lives of humans.

The old house may still have secrets. For example, were the recluses there when Wild Bill Hickok lived in the house? Could that have been why the brave Western hero left? Who knows—the recluses aren't talking.

Verify Prediction

○ CORRECT

○ INCORRECT

Summarize

....

....

....

....

....

Vocabulary Review

Word 1

Definition

Word 2

Definition

Word 3

Definition

Word 4

Definition

	Active Participation	Interactive Reader	Critical Thinking Application	Week 13 Total
TOTAL POINTS FOR WEEK 13				

RISING OUT OF THE FLOOD

By Kathleen Thompson

Build Background

Shamarr Allen grew up in a neighborhood in warm, sunny New Orleans, Louisiana. On Jourdan Avenue in the Lower Ninth Ward, everybody knew everybody. Kids played together in the street and slept over at each other's houses. People sat out on their porches in the summer. They dropped in on neighbors to visit over a glass of iced tea. It wasn't a fancy place, but it was warm with good feelings.

Allen spent most of his time on Jourdan Avenue with his friend Dinerral Shavers. They were together so much people thought they were brothers. "We told everybody we were brothers," says Allen. "My dad would always pick the both of us up in the morning and bring us to school, and he and ma would pick the both of us up in the evening and bring us home. We always were together."

Both Dinerral and Shamarr loved music. Shamarr's father, Keith Allen, played a Louis Armstrong record for Shamarr once. "I was like, 'Dad, whatever he's playing, I want to play that.' It seemed like he was having so much fun with his singing and his playing, the way the band played." After that, Allen learned to play the trumpet. He and Shavers formed a band. They hung around jazz musicians and learned from them. Then they started playing with them. The neighborhood was proud of Allen and his friend.

Generate Questions

Rising Out of the Flood

That neighborhood is haunted with memories now. Hurricane Katrina changed it forever.

When Katrina first appeared, it was just beginning to be a storm. That was on August 23, 2005, about 350 miles east of Miami. For two days, it got stronger and stronger. Then it hit Florida. By this time it had been **upgraded.** It was a Category 1 hurricane.

Fewer than eight hours later, Hurricane Katrina left land for the Gulf of Mexico. Over the warm waters, it got even stronger. On August 27, it became a Category 3 hurricane. Its winds were now more than 115 miles per hour. It covered almost the whole Gulf of Mexico. This was a very big hurricane. Shamarr Allen didn't know it yet, but Katrina was big enough to change his life.

The hurricane hit land about forty-five miles southeast of New Orleans. In late morning, it slammed inland again. This time, it created a wave that was more than twenty-six feet tall. Two Mississippi towns were hit by the wave. They were terribly damaged.

In New Orleans, people thought they would be safe. Katrina was not going to make a direct hit on the city. But a lot of New Orleans is below sea level. Big walls called **levees** keep out the waters of Lake Pontchartrain and Lake Borgne. Katrina's huge wave, added to about ten inches of rain, broke the levees. On August 29, flood waters rushed into the neighborhood with amazing force. They smashed Shamarr Allen's house into splinters.

Rising Out of the Flood

Word:

Definition:

Word:

Definition:

Allen's neighborhood was one of the first to go. Luckily the mayor of New Orleans had ordered everyone out of the city. About 1.2 million people left before the waters hit. The Allen family was among them. Thousands of others couldn't leave. Some wouldn't leave. Television cameras recorded the destruction of the Allen home. News shows played the **footage** over and over. The Allen family had to watch their house being smashed again and again on the news.

By August 30, about 80 percent of New Orleans was underwater. **Disaster** had hit the city. People crowded into any space that was above water. About 30,000 of them filled the Superdome. There wasn't enough food or clean water. People were in a terrible situation. By October 11, United States army engineers had drained the last of the flood waters from the city. But New Orleans was almost destroyed.

Generate Questions

Rising Out of the Flood

Allen lived for a year in Atlanta, Georgia. He supported himself as a musician. But he couldn't forget New Orleans. When he got back to his hometown, the only place he could find to live was with two other guys in a trailer. His friend Shavers, a fine man with a family and a successful career, was gone. He had been murdered the year before. Allen joined a group called Silence is Violence in order to honor his friend.

Then things began to happen for Allen. He got a home in the Habitat for Humanity Musicians' Village for himself and his eight-year-old son. He formed a musical partnership with an older musician named Paul Sanchez. Because of a group called Threadhead Records, Allen was able to make a CD. And then he made another. Not long ago, he sat at the Grammys ceremony with his friend Trombone Shorty. "Shorty says, 'Did you ever think when we were playing in the Quarter that we would be right here right now?' I said, 'It's what we've been dreaming about all our lives.'" It was a dream Katrina couldn't smash.

Verify Prediction

○ CORRECT

○ INCORRECT

Summarize

_____

_____

_____

_____

_____

Vocabulary Review

Sentence The _____ of the house fire was sad.

Sentence The storm was _____ to a Category 2 when the wind started to blow harder.

Sentence The earthquake in China was a _____.

Sentence The _____ were supposed to protect the city, but they failed.

	Active Participation	Interactive Reader	Critical Thinking Application	Week 14 Total
TOTAL POINTS FOR WEEK 14				

The Great
Chicken Debacle
PART ONE

By Phyllis Reynolds Naylor

Build Background

You had to be four feet tall to ride the Screaming Cyclone, Cornelia heard, but by standing as straight as possible, she was sure she would measure up.

Charles, of course, would only be tall enough to ride the Red Devil, and Mindy simply wanted to ride the merry-go-round, which was supposed to be one of the fanciest merry-go-rounds in the world. But the three Morgan children **longed** to go to Starlight Park even more than they longed for Christmas. It was all kids talked about at school.

"No! No! No!" their father had told them. "I'd rather be buried in mud up to my armpits! The crowds! The noise! The traffic!"

Mother agreed. "Just *looking* at those rides makes me dizzy," she'd said. "We'll find other things to do this summer."

"So what are we going to do?" Charles asked her as they walked home the last day of school.

"What happens to parents, anyway?" Charles grumbled. "Once they grow up, they don't have any fun."

"I guess they're just too busy taking care of us," sighed Mindy.

"I'm going to talk to Dad again," she said. "Maybe we could make a **bargain.** Wash his car ten times or something if he'll take us."

Generate Questions

"We could vacuum the inside of it too," Charles suggested.

"And shine his shoes," said Cornelia.

Mindy stopped skipping. "Maybe I don't want to go to Starlight Park after all," she said.

"Yes, you do!" cried Cornelia and Charles together.

"We *all* want to go," said Cornelia, "and we've got to find a way to make it happen."

After dinner that evening, with Charles and Mindy watching from the bushes and Mother reading up in her room, Cornelia went out on the back porch and sat down beside her dad in the swing.

The problem wasn't that Father didn't like to have fun, she decided. Cornelia could remember the time her parents woke her and Charles and Mindy because it was snowing, and they all went sledding at midnight. And the Halloween that her parents went out the back door, put on masks, and rang the front doorbell, asking Mindy for a "trick or treat." They always gave wild and crazy gifts to each other on their birthdays, too, and this caused lots of laughter when they'd gathered for celebrations back on Grandpa's farm. The trouble was they just didn't like amusement parks, *in any way, shape, or form,* Father always said.

"How was your last day of fifth grade?" he asked Cornelia as she pushed her feet against the floor to give the swing a boost.

"It was okay," she told him.

The Great Chicken Debacle—Part One

And then, before she could say anymore, before she could even mention the Screaming Cyclone, her father began to chuckle. "Your mother's birthday is only a week off," he said, "and I've been thinking about getting her a present that would remind her of the farm."

Cornelia smiled too. "You could always buy her a sheep," she suggested.

Father grinned even wider and **propped** his feet on the railing. "I bought a house with the largest yard we could afford," he said, "but there's not enough grass for a sheep."

"A horse?" Cornelia asked. "We could feed it oats." She tried to imagine her father riding a horse up to the front steps on Mother's birthday.

"No, not a horse," said Father, laughing. "I'd like to give her a chicken."

"A chicken!" cried Cornelia.

He nodded. "I know a man who's selling his poultry business. It's up for auction, and he said he'd give me a chicken. But there's one little problem: I have to get it tomorrow. Everything has to go. As soon as the auction's over, he's leaving for Maine."

"So?" said Cornelia.

"So how do I hide a chicken from your mother for a whole week?"

Cornelia's heart began to race, and goose bumps traveled up and down her spine. *Screaming Cyclone, here I come!* she told herself. "What if I said I could hide it till Mom's birthday?" she asked.

"Ha! You and who else?"

Generate Questions

"Charles and Mindy, that's who."

"Fat chance," said her father.

"But what if we could?"

"Then I'd be a **heap** grateful, that's what."

"Nope!" said Cornelia. "You'd have to do better than that."

"Five bucks?"

"Nope."

"Ten?"

"Nope."

"Hey! What are you holding out for?" asked Father.

"The Screaming Cyclone at Starlight Park," said Cornelia. "The day after Mother's birthday."

Her father groaned. Finally he said, "Well, I want something fun, and I can't think of anything crazier to give her, but chickens have to be fed and watered, you know."

"I know," said Cornelia.

"They're noisy. They cluck."

"I know," said Cornelia.

"They poop," said her father.

"I know," she said.

"And once I brought that chicken home, I wouldn't want to see it, hear it, or even think about it till the morning of Mother's birthday. Do you really think you could do that?"

"I really do," said Cornelia, though not at all sure.

"Then you've got yourself a deal," he told her.

And out in the bushes, Charles and Mindy gave each other a high five.

Verify Prediction

○ CORRECT

○ INCORRECT

Summarize

....

....

....

....

....

Vocabulary Review

Word 1

Sentence

Word 2

Sentence

Word 3

Sentence

Word 4

Sentence

	Active Participation	Interactive Reader	Critical Thinking Application	Week 15 Total
TOTAL POINTS FOR WEEK 15				

The Great Chicken Debacle
PART TWO

By Phyllis Reynolds Naylor

Build Background

When Deeter Delaney saw the three Morgans heading toward the woods, he followed, and soon all four children were sitting along the bank of the creek with their feet in the water.

"So what's up?" asked Deeter.

Cornelia's brown eyes sparkled like fireflies. "We've got a chance to go to Starlight Park, but it's going to take a lot of work," she announced. Cornelia was good at announcing. Whenever she had something to say, it came out sounding like the Ten Commandments. "Dad is going to give Mom a chicken for her birthday. All we have to do is feed it and keep it hidden for a week, and he'll take us to Starlight Park."

Deeter scratched his head. "Why is he giving her a *live* one?"

Cornelia shrugged. "They give each other crazy presents," she said.

"And he wants to give her something that will remind her of the farm," said Charles. "She always liked the farm." Charles missed the farm too. He missed riding out to Grandpa and Grandma Wheeler's every weekend for huge Sunday dinners with the rest of Mom's family, where there was corn on the cob, baked ham, blueberry and custard pies . . . No food in all the world, according to Charles, could equal the food on the farm in Iowa. And Charles was always thinking of food.

Generate Questions

"So what's the problem?" asked Deeter.

"The problem is, where are we going to hide a chicken? It will have to be fed and watered and cleaned up after. Mom mustn't see so much as a feather or hear a cluck till her birthday. We will have to keep it spectacularly secret." Cornelia had been in the **advanced** class at school, and *spectacular* was on the advanced spelling list.

They were all quiet for what seemed like a very long time, their foreheads **wrinkled** in concentration. Finally Deeter said, "Maybe we could hide it in our shed."

"Really?" asked Cornelia, wondering why she hadn't thought of that herself.

"I could ask," said Deeter.

"*Ask!*" Cornelia commanded.

Deeter started toward his house to ask his mom if they could use the shed, but suddenly he turned around and came back.

"So what's wrong? Why didn't you ask?" Cornelia wanted to know.

"Mom couldn't keep a secret if it were glued to her chin," Deeter said. "If I told her about the chicken, your mom would know by tomorrow morning."

Cornelia's face fell. "Then what are we going to do?"

The Great Chicken Debacle–Part Two

This was Deeter Delaney's finest moment: "We'll just hide it in our shed anyway. Mom never comes back here, and I'll help you take care of it."

"Deeter," said Cornelia, "you are stupendously wonderful!" *Stupendous* was another word on the advanced reading list, and Cornelia used it whenever she could.

"And nobody," she continued, looking directly at Mindy, then at Charles, "is going to even hint about any of this to Mom."

The next day, Saturday, the Morgan children didn't go outside. They didn't ride their bikes, didn't go **wading,** didn't do much of anything except sit around the house waiting for their father to come back. The plan was that he would take the chicken over to the shed and the four children would meet him there. They were so excited it was hard to sit still.

"For goodness sake, it's vacation!" Mother said, coming downstairs. "Why on earth are you sitting inside?"

"It's too hot out there," said Cornelia, trying to think of an excuse.

"It's only eighty degrees!" Mother told her.

"It's too noisy," said Charles.

"Birds? *Noisy?*" exclaimed Mother.

Generate Questions

"There are too many worms," offered Mindy.

"Worms! Am I going to have three children moping about the house for three months just because it's *summer*?" Mother cried in disbelief.

"Well, if we had chickens, they'd eat the worms," said Mindy.

Cornelia **jabbed** Mindy with her elbow, but Mother was already on her way to the kitchen, shaking her head.

At that very moment they heard their father's car coming down the street.

Charles and Mindy leaped off the couch and tumbled after Cornelia, who was already racing through the kitchen toward the back door.

"I think I feel a breeze," Cornelia called to their mother.

"A *quiet* breeze," said Charles.

"And *allll* the worms have gone back in their holes," said Mindy. "You'll be surprised, Mom, even if it *does* poop."

Mrs. Morgan stood at the window looking at them as they scurried across the yard and over to the neighbor's.

"I have the strangest children in the whole world," she murmured.

Summarize

....

....

....

....

....

Word 1

Definition

Word 2

Definition

Word 3

Definition

Word 4

Definition

	Active Participation	Interactive Reader	Critical Thinking Application	Week 16 Total
TOTAL POINTS FOR WEEK 16				

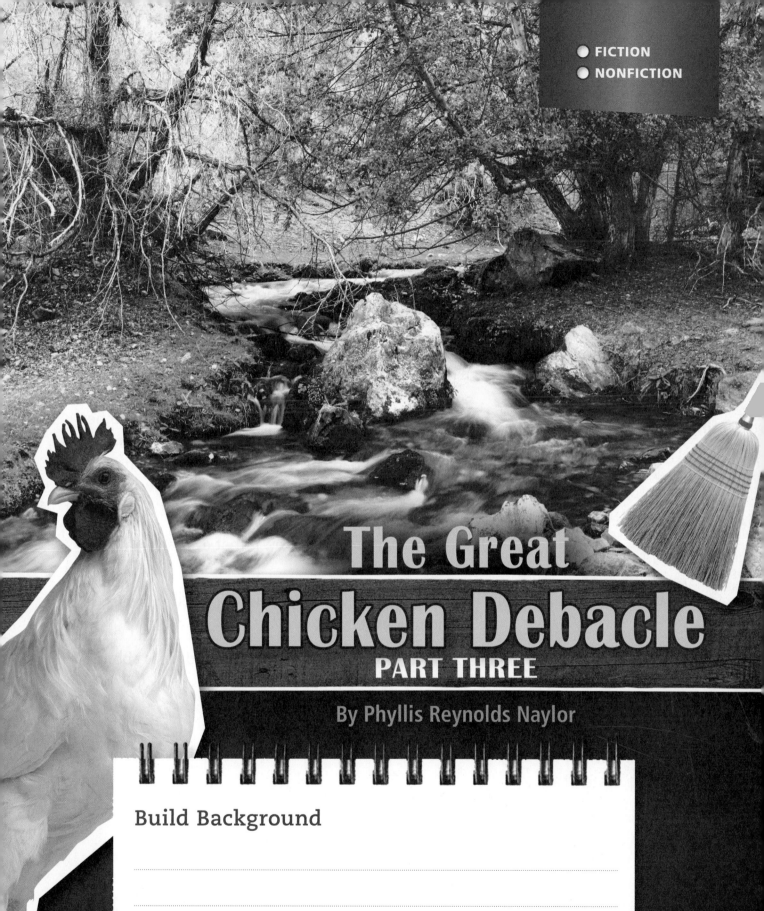

The Great
Chicken Debacle
PART THREE

By Phyllis Reynolds Naylor

Build Background

Word:

Definition:

Word:

Definition:

As soon as they were out of sight, Cornelia turned and grabbed Mindy by the arm.

"You almost gave it away!" she **scolded.**

The three of them started off again across the Delaneys' yard, through the cluster of walnut trees and the bushes near the back, and over to the old shed in one corner.

Their father was standing just inside looking down at a chicken, and Deeter was spreading a handful of grain across the bare dirt floor.

It was, Cornelia thought, the ugliest chicken she had ever seen. It was supposed to be white, she guessed, but its feathers were dirty looking. Its black eyes, surrounded by pink and gold, were lopsided or cockeyed. Half its tail feathers drooped, and the others stuck straight up in the air like a sail. The red comb on top of its head had crusty patches, and one of its legs was crooked. But then, maybe that was the way chickens were supposed to look.

Then Charles said it: "Boy, is that ever an ugly chicken!"

But Father only laughed. "Isn't it, though? Helen's going to love it!"

Grown-ups certainly had some weird ideas about fun, Cornelia decided.

Generate Questions

"It's a leghorn. A pullet," her father went on. "Bet it was the runt of the lot. But she's just about old enough to lay eggs."

"I'd better get home or Helen will suspect something," Father said. "But remember, don't come to me with your problems over this chicken. It's your job to take care of it and keep it a secret. If you kids can manage to do that, Deeter included, I'll take you all to Starlight Park."

He gave them a thumbs up and a **doubtful** grin, then left the shed and closed the door.

Cornelia, Charles, Mindy, and Deeter sat down on the floor in a circle, letting the cockeyed chicken walk around in the middle, scratching at the dirt with her wide yellow feet, pecking now and then at the ground, and thrusting out her neck with each step.

"It's like she's marching," said Deeter, smiling.

"What are we going to call her?" asked Mindy.

"We could call her 'dumpling,'" said Charles. "As in 'chicken and dumplings.' "

"It's Mom's gift. She can name the chicken herself," Cornelia told them.

But Deeter said, "We have to call her something. Until next Friday, let's call her 'No-Name.' "

"Where will she lay her eggs?" Cornelia asked.

Make Prediction

99

Word:

Definition:

Word:

Definition:

"We could set a **skillet** on the ground and she could drop her eggs in that," said Charles eagerly.

But Deeter shook his head. "We've got to make a nest for her. Hens like boxes with straw in them."

"I'll find a box she can use as a nest if you and Deeter will find something to use for straw," Cornelia told Charles.

"What should *I* do?" asked Mindy.

"You stay here and keep her company," said Cornelia. "And make sure the door stays closed."

Mindy was happy to be the chicken-sitter, and while Cornelia went home to search for a box, Charles and Deeter went to the Morgan's garage to look for something they could use for straw.

They thought about using wood shavings or even grass. But suddenly Charles' eye fell on the broom hanging on the wall beside the rake. The broom had **bristles,** long bristles, that looked like straw, felt like straw, and—for all Charles knew—were straw.

There were footsteps outside, and the boys froze as the garage door opened.

"What's taking so long?" asked Cornelia, stepping inside. Then she saw the remains of the broom on the floor.

"Charles!" she gasped. "Mom's new broom!"

Cornelia had to admit it was probably the best they could do, so they gathered up all the bristles, wrapped them in Deeter's shirt, and started across the yard toward the Delaneys' shed.

Generate Questions

"Cornelia? Charles?" Mother called from the back porch. "You're keeping an eye on Mindy, aren't you?"

"We know right where she is," Charles answered. But they didn't know at all, because when they reached the shed, the door was closed, but Mindy and the cockeyed chicken were gone.

"A chicken-napper!" said Deeter, his eyes huge.

"But where's Mindy?" Cornelia wailed. "I'm supposed to be looking after her."

"I guess somebody just walked in and kidnapped them both," said Charles. Cornelia gave a little shriek.

Deeter was already playing detective. He opened the door and crawled outside on his hands and knees, checking the ground for chicken feathers. Cornelia merely groaned when he triumphantly held a white one up in the air.

Cornelia began to panic, but Deeter pounced on still another feather. "Aha!" he said. "Look where I found this one! On the path to the creek, not the path to your yard."

Cornelia and Charles followed along behind Deeter as he crawled through the weeds on his hands and knees like a bloodhound.

"Why don't you try barking while you're at it?" Cornelia said, not nice at all, and was instantly sorry because there, coming along the path from the woods was Mindy, holding the World's Ugliest Chicken in her arms.

Verify Prediction

○ CORRECT

○ INCORRECT

Summarize

....

....

....

....

Vocabulary Review

Sentence   My mother put bacon in the   and cooked it.

Sentence   When I saw how high the fence was, I was   I could climb over it.

Sentence   The stiff   made it easy to sweep up the sand.

Sentence   When I left the door open, my father   me because the cold air came into the house.

	Active Participation	Interactive Reader	Critical Thinking Application	Week 17 Total
TOTAL POINTS FOR WEEK 17				

William Halstead
The Father of Modern Surgery

By Troy Markham

Build Background

Word:

Definition:

Word:

Definition:

Today we take a lot of things for granted when we need to have surgery. You feel confident that your doctor will have a clean operating room. You hope everyone will wash their hands and that all the tools will be **sterilized.** You also know that your doctor will try very hard to make you comfortable and check on you regularly.

But this was not always the case. Long ago it was common to expect a lot of pain during surgery. There were no drugs to make you feel better. Even worse, there was no concern about keeping things clean. Imagine if your doctor used a knife to operate on you that had been used earlier on someone else! Long ago, that was common.

We have Dr. William Halsted to thank for changing the way modern medicine is practiced. His drive to experiment led to some very important improvements in medicine. His bold nature and manner shocked others. But his discoveries have made him into a legend. He is often called "the father of modern surgery."

Generate Questions

Halsted was born into a family with a large business. But he followed his desire to study medicine instead. He sought out the best doctors to learn from in medical school and even traveled to Europe to learn the medical procedures used there.

Upon his return in 1880, he began practicing surgery at several hospitals in New York. He soon gained a reputation for outlandish and risky experiments. When his mother suffered a gallbladder attack, he performed surgery on her on the kitchen table!

Halsted also pioneered the practice of blood transfusions (transfers of blood from one person into another person). After his sister gave birth, she began losing an **alarming** amount of blood. Halsted sensed that her life was in danger. Acting quickly, he withdrew some of his own blood and transferred it into her. He then operated on her and saved her life.

When you picture a surgeon operating, what do you see on his or her hands? The thin rubber gloves surgeons wear today were invented by Halsted. Halsted insisted on keeping everything sterile. His nurses complained that they were developing rashes on their skin. The rashes were caused by the germ-killing chemicals the nurses used to wash their hands. Halsted talked to the Goodyear Rubber Company that made car tires. He asked them to make rubber gloves that could be used by doctors and nurses.

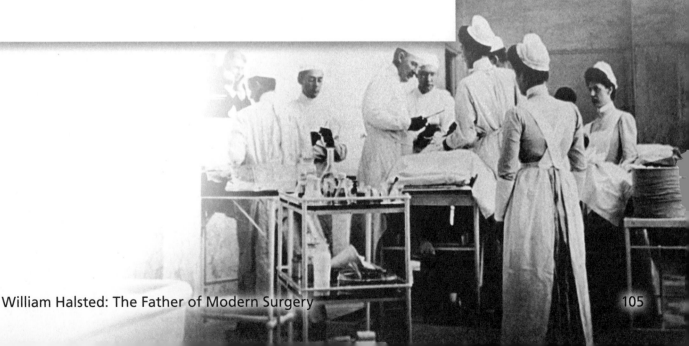

William Halsted: The Father of Modern Surgery

The gloves were very effective. The rubber surface actually improved the ability to grip surgical tools and allowed the doctor to work with precision. The gloves became so popular that soon everyone was using them. Now you would never see surgeons and nurses without them during an operation.

He joked about the gloves later in life. Halsted admitted that he had never considered how they would help the patient. At the time, he was concerned only with protecting his hands. It was a lucky accident that the gloves also provided a germ **barrier** to the patient.

One of the most important discoveries he made was the use of pain-killing medicine. He and other doctors began experimenting with various drugs. They found that if these drugs were used correctly, they could deaden pain during surgery. How did Halsted discover this? He experimented on his own body.

His experiments with pain medicines cost him dearly, though. Through these experiments he became addicted to some of those drugs. At one point, his addictions were so powerful hospitals would not hire him. He stopped practicing medicine and enrolled in a treatment program for help.

Halsted was a changed man. Upon his return, the other doctors embraced him and returned him to his position.

Generate Questions

William Halsted: The Father of Modern Surgery

Halsted remained energetic. He refused to accept that things could not be improved. Always looking for a better way to treat patients, he could be demanding. As he grew older, he became a well-respected teacher. He pushed his students hard, but his tutoring produced some of the best doctors in the world.

William Halsted died in 1922. His last years were spent shaping the way surgeons learned at Johns Hopkins Hospital. He is recognized as one of the greatest doctors in history. His accomplishments are numerous.

Thanks to Halsted, patients now receive anesthesia to eliminate intense pain during surgery. His surgical procedures have allowed doctors to save many lives. People recover from surgery more quickly and have fewer infections.

And yet many doctors say Halsted's greatest contributions to medicine are not obvious. They say his lasting **legacy** is the way he helped patients and the way he viewed medicine. He pushed others to find new and better ways to treat people. And he saw patients as more than problems—he taught doctors to see them as people and to consider their perspective when treating them. His methods live on today.

Summarize

....

....

....

....

....

Word 1
Sentence

Word 2
Sentence

Word 3
Sentence

Word 4
Sentence

TOTAL POINTS FOR WEEK 18	Active Participation	Interactive Reader	Critical Thinking Application	Week 18 Total

William Halsted: The Father of Modern Surgery

Escape Across the Ice

By Hilary Mac Austin

● FICTION
● NONFICTION

Build Background

On a cold, windy night in February 1838, a woman ran through the woods along the Kentucky side of the Ohio River. **Dodging** branches, she held her two-year-old son as she ran. She was a slave, and though we don't know her name, we do know her story. She has become known as Eliza.

She and her son were slaves on a farm along the Ohio River in Kentucky, a slave state. Across the river was the little town of Ripley in the free state of Ohio. Shortly before that night in February, Eliza had learned that her owner wanted to sell his slaves. She was desperate. She couldn't take the chance that she and her son would be sold to different people. The river had been frozen for a week, and Eliza planned to walk across the ice to Ripley. She had heard that a white man who lived on a high hill above Ripley would help her. From across the river she had probably seen the lantern that shone in a second-floor window. This light was a sign to escaping slaves that it was safe to go there for help. It was the home of John Rankin, an abolitionist minister, who would protect the runaways and help them escape north.

Generate Questions

It was dangerous, sometimes fatal, to help slaves escape. Even though there was no slavery in Ohio, hiding a runaway slave was illegal. Abolitionists, both black and white, were willing to risk their freedom and their lives. They knew slavery was wrong and immoral, and they had a secret network to help slaves get all the way to Canada. Only in Canada could an escaped slave really find **sanctuary.** This network was called the Underground Railroad.

The night in February, Eliza ran to a friendly white man's cabin. The news was not good. The man told the woman to go back. The ice wasn't safe, he said. It was rotten, full of cracks and air holes. But just then they heard the dogs howling. The slave catchers were after her.

Eliza had to try. Holding her baby, she ran down to the river and started to cross. The dogs' barking was louder and closer. The ice at the edge of the river was rotten, and when she stepped on it she broke through. Water slopped into her shoes, but she kept walking into the freezing river. The dogs and slave catchers didn't see or hear her. No one thought she would cross the dangerous ice, so they kept looking on the riverbank.

Vocabulary

Word:

Definition:

Word:

Definition:

Eliza soon found the edge of the river ice. She stepped up and onto it. The ice held. Holding her son tightly in her arms, she began walking across the river. Suddenly the ice cracked under her feet, the noise echoing in the darkness. Eliza struggled in the deep water. She threw her son forward onto the hard ice ahead. Desperate now, Eliza pulled herself up onto the ice, stood up, and started to run. People say that rotten ice broke under her one more time before she reached the other side. Again, she saved her son. Again, she pulled herself out of the dark, cold river. Finally she reached the other side where she fell, wet and cold, onto the muddy riverbank. Safe!

Just then a hand grabbed her arm. Chancy Shaw, a slave catcher, had been on the Ohio side of the river the whole time. He had been listening as Eliza struggled to cross the dangerous ice. All her effort had been for nothing. Eliza cried out, and so did the baby.

Then something unusual happened. Shaw helped her up and picked up the baby. He had seen what Eliza had done and was **astounded** by her bravery. "Any woman who crossed that river carrying her baby has won her freedom," he said.

Generate Questions

Shaw quietly hurried Eliza and her child through the dark streets of Ripley. Soon, the slave catcher pointed to a house on a hill, high above the town, where the famous abolitionist and conductor on the Underground Railroad, John Rankin, lived.

Rankin and his family helped Eliza and her baby. They gave them warm clothes and hot food, and that same cold night Rankin's two sons, aged 13 and 15, guided her and her son to the home of another family, the next station on the Underground Railroad. Eliza had just completed the first step of her trip to Canada and freedom.

Why is this woman known as Eliza? Years later, Rankin told the story to a friend, the writer Harriet Beecher Stowe. Stowe was so moved that she told the woman's story in her novel, *Uncle Tom's Cabin.* Stowe named her character Eliza. The book **stirred** the North to such anger over slavery that some say it helped start the Civil War. As for the real Eliza, she went back to Ripley years later, where the Rankin's helped her rescue the rest of her family from slavery in Kentucky. These ordinary people, black and white, did what they knew was right. They changed our nation.

Verify Prediction

◯ CORRECT

◯ INCORRECT

Summarize

....

....

....

....

Word 1

Definition

Word 2

Definition

Word 3

Definition

Word 4

Definition

	Active Participation	Interactive Reader	Critical Thinking Application	Week 19 Total
TOTAL POINTS FOR WEEK 19				

All in an Instant

By Kathleen Thompson

LOL !!!

!!!!!!!!

XoXo <3

Ttyl?

Y! bye, c u later

Build Background

Word:

Definition:

....

....

....

....

Word:

Definition:

....

....

....

The ping-pong ball bounced from paddle to table to paddle in a heartbeat. In the next heartbeat, it bounced back again. It was so fast most photographs would have shown it as a blur—a curve of white in the air. It was almost as fast as an instant message.

Four young men were playing and watching that ping-pong ball. Amnon Amir, Yair Goldfinger, Arik Vardi, and Sefi Visiger had each served his **compulsory** three years in the Israeli army. Then each of them had gone to work for a small software company in Herzliya, Israel. Together, the four had left the company because of a disagreement. Now, in 1996, they were **unemployed** and playing ping-pong. Sometimes they played pool. Sometimes they went to the beautiful nearby beaches. Whatever they did, there was always conversation.

They were software guys, and the Internet was an exciting place, so they mostly traded ideas about the Internet. They started looking for some kind of Internet service they could develop. And as the ping-pong ball bounced back and forth, the idea came. The four young men realized there were millions of people online at any moment in time. What if one person online could send a message to anyone else who was online? The message would travel by Internet in an instant. E-mail was the electronic version of a letter. Instant messaging (IM) would be more like a conversation. It was a brand-new idea with a lot of possibilities. No one had ever

Generate Questions

....

....

....

....

....

....

All in an Instant

thought of it before, but the young men were sure everyone would hear about it soon.

The four decided to develop the technology for their idea. They would need money, but it was such a great idea, someone would surely invest. That's what they thought. In reality, no one wanted to write a check. Then Vardi's father stepped in. Yossi Vardi was one of the founders of Israel Chemicals, so he understood about businesses and great ideas. He gave the young men several thousand dollars to work with.

Amir went to college the next fall, but the other three went to California. They went there because of the great Internet infrastructure in the area called Silicon Valley. In that area, many computer companies had sprung up, and everything was designed to help them. It was the place to go if you wanted to invent some new software that just might change the world.

The young men didn't enjoy the warm sun or the ocean sands. They didn't take trips to Disneyland or tours in large buses to the houses of the stars. The young men slept in their office and ate fast food. "We were in our submarine phase," says Goldfinger. "We didn't see TV or movies for six months. We didn't go to good restaurants. We just worked all the time. . . ."

They named their company Mirabilis, which means "marvelous" in Latin. They named their program ICQ, short for "I seek you." They finally finished a version and sent it out to forty of their friends. Seven weeks later, there were 65,000 ICQ users. It was amazing.

Mirabilis didn't have an **advertising** budget. In fact, it didn't really have a budget at all. The company was giving ICQ away. The men didn't know how they were going to make money from it. They didn't know whether they would *ever* make money, but they wanted people to use the program. Basically they just asked people to tell their friends about it. They had no idea how big it would grow.

Generate Questions

Then Yossi Vardi came to the United States and visited them. Their one and only **investor** was a very smart businessman, and he made a series of predictions about their future. He told them ICQ was going to become huge, and he was right. In May 1997, there were 850,000 ICQ users. Just less than a year later, there were nine million, and about two and a half million of those used instant messaging every day. It had become part of their way of life.

By June 1998, there were twelve million ICQ users. Vardi, Amir, Goldfinger, and Visiger sold the company to America Online (AOL). The price was $407 million.

The four men certainly had made a great deal of money. More important to them and to us, their invention opened up a new world. It was the first instant-messaging program on the Internet. Others have developed IM programs since, but ICQ is still very widely used. The military has even used it to improve communication in the Middle East.

Is ICQ as important in the history of science as the invention of the telegraph or the telephone? Does it rank with communication satellites? Maybe not. But those ping-pong players definitely changed the way people communicate with one another.

Verify Prediction

○ **CORRECT**

○ **INCORRECT**

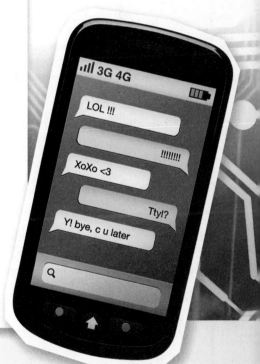

Summarize

....

....

....

....

....

Vocabulary Review

Sentence The _____ people spent a lot of time looking for jobs.

Sentence The _____ looked for a good company in which to put her money.

Sentence Serving in the military is not _____ in the United States.

Sentence The _____ for the movie made me want to see it.

	Active Participation	Interactive Reader	Critical Thinking Application	Week 20 Total
TOTAL POINTS FOR WEEK 20				

All in an Instant

Savannah

The Ghostly City that Never Sleeps

By Dennis Fertig

4

Build Background

Savannah, Georgia, is one of America's oldest cities. It is full of history, gracious old buildings, and stunning gardens. And, according to legend, it's also full of ghosts. Lots of them!

Even back in the 1880s, many Savannah citizens worried that not all the humans who **dwelled** in their houses were necessarily alive. Little Gracie Watson was a young child in those days. What did she think about ghosts? Did she wonder if they haunted the hotel her parents owned? If the stories about her are true, the answer is she probably didn't think about ghosts at all. Gracie and her parents were happy, cheerful people. They had many friends. They hosted many lively parties at the hotel. Gracie was often the center of attention at these joyous celebrations.

Still, Gracie was little and would often tire of adult gatherings. Then she would leave the party. She would play somewhat noisily underneath the hotel's back stairway. When the guests heard her playing there, they knew the party had slowed down. It was time to leave.

Then something happened. Gracie's happy life turned into a *short* happy life. Around Easter 1889, Gracie caught pneumonia. Within days, she had died. Her grieving parents buried the six-year-old in Bonaventure Cemetery. Above the little girl's grave, they erected a statue. It showed Gracie as the joyful, **exuberant** child she had been.

Generate Questions

The strange thing is that although Gracie was buried in the cemetery, people believed she still played under the stairway in the hotel. For decades, hotel guests and staff heard a child's laughter from the back of the hotel. Once again, the noise of Gracie playing told many guests something. It was time to leave. Fast!

In the 1950s, the old hotel was torn down. A new building was built on the spot. Yet people still claim to hear Gracie's happy laughter in the newer building. It comes from exactly where the old back stairway had been.

Gracie is just one of dozens of ghosts who are said to haunt Savannah. The city has been called the most haunted place in America. That might be true if ghosts are counted by the number of ghost tours and ghost experts in the city!

Make Prediction

Word:

Definition:

Word:

Definition:

Why do so many living people in Savannah think they are seeing so many dead people? Guides on ghost tours give many reasons. Savannah's long life has been filled with much sadness—the harsh treatment of enslaved African Americans, the kidnapping of young men who were forced into **crime,** terrible fires and epidemics that wiped out families. The list even includes a pseudo-scientific (methods or theories with no scientific base) reason: the old, old houses were built with materials that somehow stored energy from the past.

Not all the ghost sightings are like the ones in movies. There are apparently ghost cats slinking in and out of houses and alleys. A few people claim to have seen ghost buildings—old structures torn down long ago. Others have opened doors to unused, ancient theaters. Inside they've viewed whole audiences of people dressed in old-fashioned clothes, laughing **heartily** at something unseen on the stage. Those old plays must have been really entertaining.

Some places in Savannah are particularly well known for their long-term ghostly residents. Tour guides claim that one of Savannah's best restaurants and inns has at least two well-known ghosts who have been around a long time. The first one is named Anna. She died in Room 204 in the 1820s, brokenhearted after a failed romance. Since then many strange, scary things have happened in Room 204. The inn even used to require guests to sign a paper that made it clear they had to pay for the room even if they were frightened away.

Generate Questions

When she was alive, Anna liked nice clothes. Female inn guests often claimed that Anna's spirit "borrowed" clothing from their luggage. Guides on ghost tours like to tell that one year Anna even decorated a Christmas tree with the clothing of some female guests she didn't like.

Tour guides say the inn also has a second ghost, another female. This one was a former servant from the 1850s who is much angrier than Anna. Occasionally modern-day inn employees believe they feel pushes and pinches from this spirit. Some employees are afraid to go into certain storage areas alone because of her. Waitresses in the inn's restaurant even think this ghost steals their written food orders before the chef sees them.

There are many, many ghost stories in Savannah. Some are just a little creepy. Some will keep you up for nights. Yet as frightening as the tales of the dead are, people love Savannah ghost walks. Many tourists even hope to see real ghosts.

And Savannah seems to always come up with new spookiness. The latest tale is about a ghost who steals words from stories about haunted Savannah. Just when a writer thinks the story is finished, a word is   .

Verify Prediction

◯ CORRECT

◯ INCORRECT

Summarize

Vocabulary Review

Word 1

Sentence

Word 2

Sentence

Word 3

Sentence

Word 4

Sentence

	Active Participation	Interactive Reader	Critical Thinking Application	Week 21 Total
TOTAL POINTS FOR WEEK 21				

Savannah: The Ghostly City that Never Sleeps

● FICTION
● NONFICTION

LILY B. on the BRINK OF COOL

PART ONE

By Elizabeth Cody Kimmel

Build Background

Wednesday, June 19

My room.

NOTE TO FUTURE BIOGRAPHERS: Welcome to the notebook of the soon-to-be internationally recognized writer Lily Blennerhassett. I am recording my life for the benefit of future scholars devoting their professional lives to my Collected Works and for the benefit of readers, writers, and all who Seek the Truth.

And also because this counts as a summer project for Advanced English.

Thursday, June 20

Kitchen Table. With Nutter Butter.

My life lacks excitement. It's worse than that, actually. My life lacks action. I am an uninteresting person. I lack the raw materials necessary to produce a great novel.

I blame my parents. They are simple, plain, by-the-book people. They do not take risks. They do not pick up hitchhikers. They do not sample mushrooms that grow in the wild. They are so **mainstream,** they make The First Lady look radical.

Take driving with my father, for example. I may be only thirteen, and totally lacking in driver's education, but even I know that on the highway the left lane is supposed to be the fast lane. But my father disregards this Accepted Fact of Life on a daily basis. He'll maneuver the Honda into the left lane, then cruise

Generate Questions

along at 55, the posted speed limit in most of New York State. Not 54. Never 56. And when regular people, nice average Joes, come up behind him wanting to pass, he refuses to move over to the right lane. And okay, some of these people might get a little irritated. Can you blame them? And what does my father do? Nothing at all. Just chugs along at 55 with this quiet It's a Beautiful Day in the Neighborhood expression on his face. And if you make the mistake of pointing out that someone is trying to pass, he'll just shake his head and smile. He'll point to the speedometer. He'll say, "I'm doing the legal speed limit. Nobody has any right to complain. This is the speed we're supposed to be going."

But let's not forget my mother. Somebody ought to apply for a grant to seriously study her. When my mother stays in a hotel, she *makes the beds* in the morning. I am not inventing this. Whether it's the **ritziest** place in the state or the Super 8 just off the freeway exit ramp, she always makes the beds and folds the used towels neatly on the rack. She claims she "can't think clearly with the beds unmade." I don't need therapy to know the real issue is how our family appears to other people. Unmade beds are untidy, and the last thing Mom wants is for word to get out to the Super 8 housekeeping staff that the Blennerhassetts from Room 118 are Untidy People.

Life in the fast lane has NEVER been worse.

Make Prediction

Lily B. on the Brink of Cool–Part One

Friday, June 21

Raining. Upstairs. Window seat.

I am waiting for Charlotte. It will be difficult saying a serious good-bye to someone who is attending Young Executive Camp for part of the summer. If it had been anyone else, I would have written a **sarcastic** short story about it and submitted it to *The New Yorker.* But it is more complicated than that.

Charlotte and I have spent every summer together since we were in kindergarten and became best friends. First it was Fairy Day Camp, then it was Sports Center Intensive Swim Program. Somewhere around the third or fourth grade we did the Brownie/Girl Scout thing. And for the last several years Camp Migawam. We slept in a cabin together, canoed together, swam together, launched butter pats at the ceiling in the dining room. Together.

I realize it isn't Charlotte's fault, necessarily, that Camp Migawam went out of business after Charlotte called the newspaper regarding the offering of bribes by camp administrators to the state health and safety inspector. But when it came time for us to pick a new way to spend the summer, Charlotte got all flipped out about this new alternative camp she'd found out about on the web, where Chief Executive Officers and Business **Tycoons** of tomorrow come together for the purpose of "educational enrichment." I looked at the brochure, just to see. It was appalling! No canoes. No

Generate Questions

Lily B. on the Brink of Cool–Part One

cabins. No swimming, no sailing, no archery, not even any nature walks. Instead, the brochure talked about seminars, interactive workshops, and lectures by visiting corporate leaders. In short, it was a nightmare.

I kept thinking she'd come to her senses. I kept thinking we'd find some nice tennis camp, or a riding program, or a hiking trip for girls. But Charlotte wouldn't budge. She was determined to enroll in Young Executive Camp. Spending a large part of the summer without Charlotte would be a disaster. But let's face it— me at Young Executive Camp would be a *catastrophe.*

I am going to be a writer. And if circumstances become difficult, and my genius is not immediately recognized, and it becomes unpleasantly necessary for me to take on some additional work, there are several jobs I feel qualified for and interested in (in which I feel interested and for which I feel qualified?) (for and in which I feel qualified and interested? Future Biographers: You decide).

Verify Prediction

○ CORRECT

○ INCORRECT

Summarize

....

....

....

....

....

Word 1

Definition

Word 2

Definition

Word 3

Definition

Word 4

Definition

TOTAL POINTS FOR WEEK 22	Active Participation	Interactive Reader	Critical Thinking Application	Week 22 Total

LILY B. on the BRINK OF COOL

PART TWO

By Elizabeth Cody Kimmel

● FICTION
● NONFICTION

Build Background

So you understand, Future Biographers, why I cannot go to camp with Charlotte, **despite** the fact that I will be left alone with my sadly unexciting parents, and despite the fact that my parents have found no suitable alternative to Camp Migawam at this late date and have only very grudgingly allowed me to stay home because of my persuasive and persistent argument that this notebook, my Advanced English summer project, will require all my free time and, once completed, will virtually guarantee my place on the Honor Roll. And I only agreed to write down these *highly* confidential things because I simply have to show my English teacher that I have kept this notebook, and am not required to allow anyone to actually read it. That's a privilege I'm saving for you, Future Biographers.

Sunday, June 23

Bedroom. Eavesdropping on parents downstairs through heating vent.

8:29 a.m. Years of mornings monitoring conversations through the vent may finally be paying off. Something is up, Future Biographers!

8:30 a.m. I'm hearing the name Delia. (The heating vent gives me only a 50% accurate version of conversations).

Generate Questions

8:32 a.m. There it is again, The Delia Drop. I'm sure the Blennerhassett Institute (when it is founded) will have all this family information, Future Biographers (may I call you F.B.s? It's easier to write). But for your ease and research convenience, I'll **divulge** Delia's identity. She's my mother's brother's daughter (read: NOT A BLENNERHASSETT). I see her on holidays, mostly. She gives age-inappropriate gifts (last Christmas she gave me a set of Little Mermaid paints). She arrives late and leaves early to go back to work (she's a lawyer). She makes and receives numerous calls to and from clients on her cell phone, even at the dinner table (she's a workaholic). And from what I can tell, a large portion of her life is about food. Avoiding it, getting fat-free versions of it, running to the gym to work it off. It's insane. The woman is a size 2. I've seen bigger hips on PEZ dispensers.

8:35 a.m. Delia is apparently buying some webbing. Maybe she's going to start a side business making dog leashes? Or harnesses? What else can you do with webbing? Fishing nets?

8:37 a.m. The webbing is apparently causing quite a bit of excitement. My mother is talking so fast, I can hardly make out what she's saying.

8:39 a.m. Apparently this is a very expensive webbing. How many feet of webbing is she buying? How many leashes can one skinny girl make?

Lily B. on the Brink of Cool—Part Two

135

8:41 a.m. My mother and father seem to be agreeing that Delia is getting **harried.** The webbing project must be overwhelming her.

8:42 a.m. Oh.

8:43 a.m. *Oh.*

8:44 a.m. OH.

8:45 a.m. I had thought now that Charlotte's gone, I'd hit rock bottom immediately and stay there. But apparently I'm going to plunge even lower. Delia is getting married, and it sounds like the Blennerhassetts will be attending the wedding. Forget everything you've read, because unless maybe it's your own, a wedding is the most boring thing in the universe. I know. I went to one two years ago—my mother's hairdresser married a shampoo-and-conditioner sales rep—and I still get flashbacks when I walk past the salon. They served ravioli over rice. The bridesmaids wore pastel taffeta. The band played "If You're Happy and You Know It, Clap Your Hands." We were forced to participate in a conga line! Is it possible for me to develop strep throat simply by wanting it very, very badly?

Monday, June 24

I'm at The Dress Barn in the Young Miss section and changing room.

The horrors of clothes shopping. Where does my mother find these things? She **whisks** into the dressing room and hands me items triumphantly, like she's Donatella Versace previewing her new line. The only thing is, the outfits she's bringing in for me to try on look like they were made for one of those American Girl dolls. Ruffly stuff. High collars. Puffed sleeves. Like I'm getting ready for a *Masterpiece Theatre* audition. Who wants to walk around looking like they were sucked into some giant, girl-eating doily?

1:15 p.m. I won't try that on.

1:16 p.m. SHE CAN'T MAKE ME TRY THAT ON.

1:20 p.m. My self-esteem has never been lower. I can hardly bring myself to write about it. It was . . . shiny. Green. Lace collar, poofed-out skirt. An ABOMINATION. A lampshade with sleeves. The only way to get her to take it away was to try it on. I made sure to slouch and hunch over so that it wouldn't fit right. After all, my mother is a reasonable person. Clearly she could see that with me inside it, the dress was . . . awful. Tonight I'll call Charlotte, and we'll laugh about it. It *is* kind of funny. Some poor soul actually designed that dress, and maybe even took it home to show their mom. Charlotte will bust a gut laughing. No one appreciates a fashion disaster quite like Charlotte.

1:30 p.m. My mother BOUGHT the dress. She said it will be perfect for the wedding. She said I will look "darling."

Charlotte must never, *never* know about this.

Summarize

_____

_____

_____

_____

_____

Lily B. on the Brink of Cool—Part Two

Vocabulary Review

Sentence The waitress was _____ because there were so many people shouting orders at her.

Sentence My mother always _____ into the room after she gets home from work.

Sentence I promised I would not _____ the secret.

Sentence I went to the party _____ feeling sick.

	Active Participation	Interactive Reader	Critical Thinking Application	Week 23 Total
TOTAL POINTS FOR WEEK 23				

LILY B. on the BRINK OF COOL

PART THREE

By Elizabeth Cody Kimmel

Build Background

Friday, June 28

Hour of departure for wedding approaches.

11:32 a.m. The Lampshade with Sleeves has been secured in garment bag and placed in Honda. Sadly, the chances of this dress being lost, damaged, or mutilated before the wedding are growing even slimmer than Delia.

11:50 a.m. Keys to Honda are missing.

11:59 a.m. Lunch being served—fat-free turkey on whole-grain bread, apple slices, vegetable juice.

12:31 p.m. Frequent commands for all Blennerhassetts to visit the bathroom before departure continue to be issued.

12:40 p.m. Keys to the Honda still missing.

12:48 p.m. Last bag placed in trunk. Road-map collection placed in glove compartment. Lunch dishes cleared away, scoured, and sterilized. Table and kitchen surfaces rubbed violently with antibacterial cleanser.

12:50 p.m. Keys to Honda still missing.

12:55 p.m. Final house check occurring—lights out, coffee machine unplugged, windows locked, shades down, all faucets and water-bearing devices firmly in the off position, beds made neatly (so that any thieves breaking and entering during our absence will not think the Blennerhassetts are Untidy People).

Generate Questions

Lily B. on the Brink of Cool—Part Three

12:59 p.m. Keys to the Honda located in my bathroom behind the soap dish. Discussion **ensues** as to how they got there. No explanation is forthcoming. I suggest the whole episode be filed under L, for Life's Little Mysteries, right next to the Loch Ness Monster.

Backseat of Honda.

2:30 p.m. Note to self—when legally adult (18? 21?), vow never again to **tolerate** the playing of Broadway's greatest hits on any car trip.

3:10 p.m. Wrong exit taken from freeway. Parents exhibiting signs of nervous agitation and veiled hostility.

3:26 p.m. Back on freeway.

3:50 p.m. Exit relocated and taken. Hotel in sight.

5:55 p.m. Well, it's a fancy place anyway. Two-bedroom suite means two enormous beds for Mom to make tomorrow morning. Plush carpet. Coffeemaker in the bathroom. Attractive mahogany wardrobe that opens to reveal wide-screen television set. No time to ponder the origins of the rehearsal dinner, as we are expected at Olivieri's Trattoria down the street for said ritual in thirty-five minutes. From what I can pick up, I understand it's a traditional, night-before-the-wedding dinner where all the relatives show up, possibly to make sure the whole gang can get through three hours in one another's company without resorting to verbal or physical abuse.

Lily B. on the Brink of Cool–Part Three

The unimportant relatives' table; Olivieri's Trattoria, rehearsal dinner.

6:37 p.m.

AUNT TIFFY: And is this Lily? Can I believe my eyes?

(I look around helplessly, hoping another Lily is standing behind me and clothed in something better than the mock turtleneck and striped skirt I am unhappily wearing.)

AUNT TIFFY: Let me look at you! Don't you look darling!

(This cannot be said for Aunt Tiffy, who resembles a marshmallow sporting an inexpensive wig.)

ME: *(mumbling):* Thank you.

AUNT TIFFY: Stand up. Let me get a really good look at you.

(I am speechless, paralyzed with horror.)

MOM: Lily? Did you hear your Aunt Tiffy? Stand up, honey.

(I am still speechless, rising to feet on numb legs.)

AUNT TIFFY: Oh! For goodness' sake, the girl has grown two inches since Thanksgiving. And what a darling figure! Ted, come look at our Lily!

ME: *(plummeting back into sitting position before Uncle Ted appears):* Ack.

AUNT TIFFY: What did you say, dear?

MOM: Speak up, Lily. *(To the waiter)* Are there any wholegrain rolls?

Generate Questions

AUNT TIFFY: Now where has Ted gone off to? Oh, but there's Chipper. Chipper! Chipper! Chipper! Come over here and look at our Lily. She's turned into a real little lady.

*(Possible **tactics**: 1) Fake seizure 2) fake stomach virus 3) fake headache 4) reveal true feelings about Aunt Tiffy to Aunt Tiffy.)*

6:50 p.m. Saved! Saved by the arrival of the first course! Mom and Aunt Tiffy have been distracted by the nutritional concerns and are attempting to **summon** the chef to find out if the vegetable terrine can be removed, reassembled into its original vegetable form, and steamed.

6:52 p.m. Oh. F.B.s, it is even worse than I thought. A blizzard of bad dresses and clip-on ties. An accordion player is following people around, playing something that sounds like an optimistic Eastern European funeral march. Aunt Tiffy has abandoned her vegetable terrine in an attempt to find more relatives to assist in humiliating me.

SOME NOTABLE STATISTICS:

Average age of wedding guest: 50.

Average dress size: 16.

Average occupation: Men—public relations consultant. Women—*Ladies' Home Journal* subscriber.

Average condition of hair: Men—limp comb-over. Women—ten inches over top of head.

Most commonly used adjective: Men—"terrific." Women—"darling."

Most commonly asked question: Men—"How are you liking school?" Women—"How are you liking school?" HELP ME!!!!!

Verify Prediction

○ CORRECT

○ INCORRECT

Summarize

Vocabulary Review

Word 1

Sentence

Word 2

Sentence

Word 3

Sentence

Word 4

Sentence

	Active Participation	Interactive Reader	Critical Thinking Application	Week 24 Total
TOTAL POINTS FOR WEEK 24				

Lily B. on the Brink of Cool–Part Three

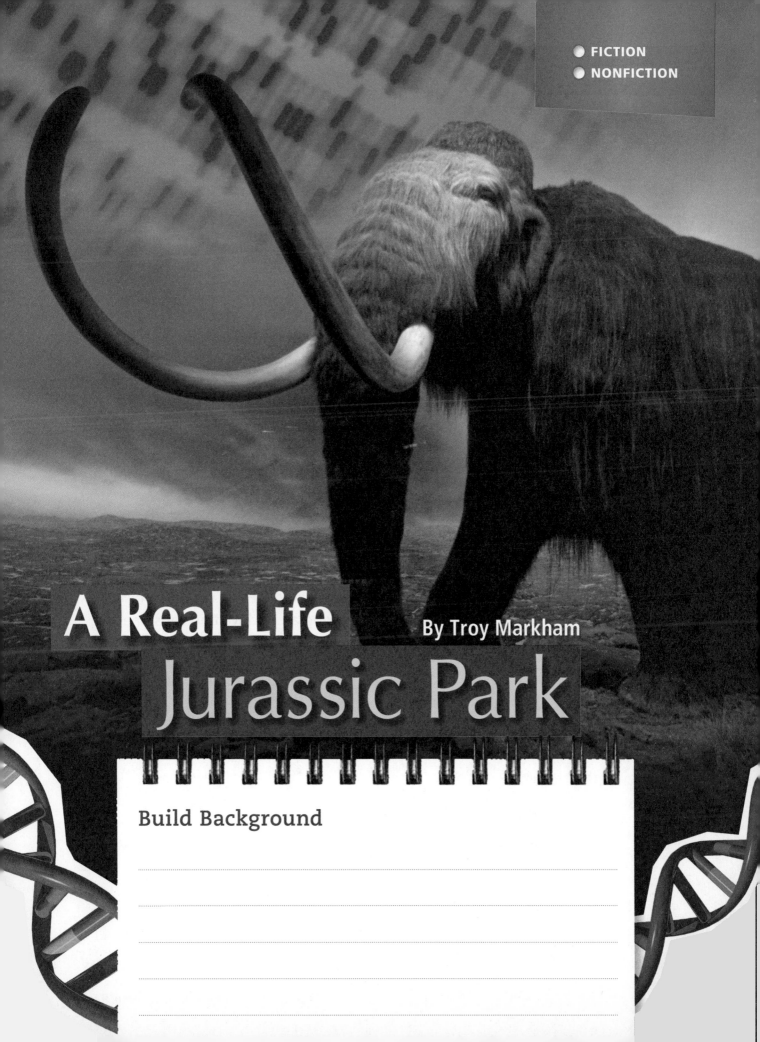

● FICTION
● NONFICTION

A Real-Life
By Troy Markham
Jurassic Park

Build Background

Word:

Definition:

Word:

Definition:

Using new technology to **clone** living dinosaurs is the stuff of dreams and science-fiction movies. Or is it? Could we possibly use DNA techniques to create our own Jurassic Park someday? Akira Iritani believes that the future is now. He plans to use DNA technology to create real, live woolly mammoths to walk among us, even though the last mammoth died outover four thousand years ago.

Iritani is a scientist at Kyoto University in Japan who works with DNA. He saw that researchers had finally been successful in cloning sheep and cattle. The techniques they used involve taking DNA from one living animal. This DNA is then placed in the egg cells of another animal. The egg cell would then grow and multiply, creating a baby animal that was an exact copy, or clone, of the animal with the extracted DNA. Iritani had seen the movie *Jurassic Park* and wondered if this could be done with animals that were no longer living. The missing link, it seemed, was having viable (capable of living) DNA.

This is actually a pretty big problem. Iritani knew that even with the fresh, perfect DNA extracted from a living sheep, the success of cloning an animal was still only about 30 percent. And let's face it . . . dinosaurs are not exactly walking around waiting for someone to take a blood sample.

Generate Questions

Most scientists dismissed Iritani's theories. How would he get **intact** dinosaur DNA when the last living examples died out millions of years ago? Their remains exist only in bone or fossil form now. Even if you could get good dinosaur DNA, they argued, there are no living mother dinosaurs in which to implant the DNA eggs. You still need a mother dinosaur to give birth.

Enter the woolly mammoth. Although mammoths have been extinct for many thousands of years, they were living recently enough that many bodies have been found frozen in ice. These bodies are still fairly intact and may contain cells with DNA that could be used. Iritani argued that with enough work, he could even find usable sperm and egg cells. The same ice that may have killed the woolly mammoths now surrounds their bodies. This ice may have preserved them to the point at which such cells may be undamaged.

But the other problem remains. How would you transplant the cells and use them to give birth to a living creature? No living woolly mammoth mothers are still around. Iritani had another theory, though. He felt that he could travel in time along the evolutionary trail for help.

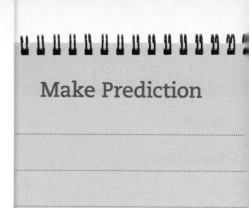

A Real-Life Jurassic Park

Word:

Definition:

Word:

Definition:

Although there are no woolly mammoths alive today, the mammoth is an ancestor of the modern-day elephant. And there are plenty of living elephants around. Could Iritani put mammoth DNA into an elephant egg cell and then transplant that egg cell into an elephant? He felt this was possible. Then the elephant could give birth to a woolly mammoth.

Other scientists are still skeptical. They point out that it may be difficult or even impossible to find woolly mammoth DNA that is undamaged. The technology of **manipulating** DNA to put it into elephant eggs is still tricky. Even if all that works, there may be big differences in elephants and mammoths that would prevent a live birth from occurring. Some scientists believe that bringing back animals from the past is just wrong.

But Iritani has succeeded in selling his idea so far. Several other scientists have joined his laboratory group in Japan. His team is ready to try. Even more important, investors have come up with the money to fund his effort. They have created the Mammoth Creation Project.

Generate Questions

Will it work? The world is waiting to see what happens. Currently his team is searching the frozen Siberian lands for frozen woolly mammoth bodies in hopes that they will find one with usable DNA.

The scientists have already found an isolated area of Siberia to serve as a nature preserve. They believe living woolly mammoths could roam freely and **inhabit** this area. Iritani believes if he can successfully bring the mammoths back from extinction, he could eventually add other extinct animals, such as saber-toothed cats. He has named his preserve "Pleistocene Park," a more modern version of Jurassic Park.

"This is an extension of my work for the past twenty years in trying to save endangered species," remarks Iritani. And he may be right. If he can bring back woolly mammoths, perhaps the future may hold promise for creatures that humans have never seen. The question many ask is not "Can we do it?" but "Should we do it?"

Verify Prediction

◯ **CORRECT**

◯ **INCORRECT**

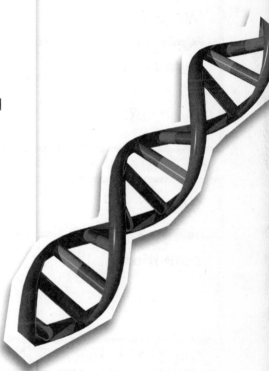

Summarize

....

....

....

....

....

....

Vocabulary Review

Word 1

Definition

Word 2

Definition

Word 3

Definition

Word 4

Definition

	Active Participation	Interactive Reader	Critical Thinking Application	Week 25 Total
TOTAL POINTS FOR WEEK 25				

Surviving the Sinking

TITANIC

By Dennis Fertig

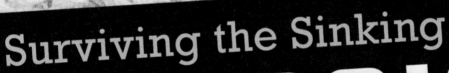

Build Background

"Sinking? Of course, *Titanic* couldn't be sinking!"

That was what Violet Jessop thought just after midnight on April 15, 1912. Jessop worked as a stewardess on *Titanic,* which was at that time the world's newest and largest ocean-traveling passenger ship. *Titanic* could carry almost three thousand travelers, plus a crew of more than eight hundred. This was the great ship's first voyage ever.

Jessop loved the sea and its mighty ships. She had been a stewardess for four years and had crossed the oceans many times in different **vessels**. But *Titanic* was special. It offered great luxury and safety, and was said to be "unsinkable."

Jessop's job was to clean cabins and corridors, like a maid in a hotel. But unlike a maid, Jessop couldn't go home at night. She lived in a small crew cabin during long voyages.

Titanic's crew cabins, like the rest of the ship, were new and fresh. Jessop was sleeping in her cabin when *Titanic's* tragedy started. At exactly twenty minutes before midnight, she heard the sound of ripping metal. The ship's big engines momentarily stopped and then started again. The crash was so small that most passengers didn't notice it.

Generate Questions

Titanic had hit an iceberg. *Titanic's* captain had worried about that very possibility, so he had set a route to avoid the Atlantic's most frigid waters. But ships sailing earlier on that route had found more icebergs than expected. *Titanic's* radio operators had received warning messages, yet failed to alert the captain.

Even so, *Titanic's* crew had searched the sea for danger. A scout had spotted an iceberg ahead and sounded an alarm. The big ship made a fast, **nimble** turn, but it wasn't quick enough, and a ragged edge of the iceberg had torn into *Titanic's* side. The contact scraped gashes into the hull near the bow and quickly allowed four thousand tons of seawater to gush into *Titanic's* lower compartments.

Even though the captain had realized what had happened and sent out SOS calls to other ships, he wasn't overly worried. *Titanic* was built to survive this kind of emergency. Doors automatically locked compartments so water wouldn't spread to other parts of the ship. *Titanic's* bow did dip a bit, but by about 12:20 A.M. the sinking had stopped. Nevertheless, passengers were awakened and told to put on life belts.

Jessop was called to duty to help reassure passengers and assist them with their life belts.

Then Jessop felt *Titanic* tilt farther forward.

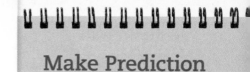

Make Prediction

Surviving the Sinking *Titanic*

Word:

Definition:

Word:

Definition:

Seawater had again found a way into the wounded ship. The worst had happened. *Titanic* began slowly slipping into the sea. At 12:40 A.M., the captain ordered passengers to board lifeboats.

Jessop was sent to the top deck to help with the lifeboats and to get ready to board herself. The deck was crammed with **frantic** people. Flares were being fired into the sky to tell other ships that *Titanic* was in distress.

The rules for boarding lifeboats were strict. Women and children were to go first. After that, men could board if there were empty seats. Many of the lifeboats could hold sixty-five people, but there were more passengers and crew than seats on lifeboats.

The lifeboats dangled eighty feet above the ocean, and many people were afraid to board. So, at first, half-empty lifeboats were lowered into the water. Later people panicked and scrambled to get into the boats. Some men were forced away at gunpoint. Women and children first!

Jessop looked at the remaining people on deck. Would they or anyone survive? Suddenly a crewmate grabbed her and led her into Lifeboat 16. He also gave her something to hold—a baby found alone, crying in the night.

Generate Questions

As Lifeboat 16 was lowered at 1:45 A.M., Jessop held the shivering infant closely. The lifeboat slowly descended past row after row of *Titanic's* lit portholes and finally splashed into the Atlantic. The few men aboard immediately dipped long oars into the water and rowed Lifeboat 16 away from the ship as fast as possible. If *Titanic* sank, it could suck the lifeboats down with it.

Around 2:15 A.M. all of *Titanic* sank beneath the sea. The unsinkable ship was gone! Cold, swirling waves now were swallowing struggling people. Jessop's boat was far away, but she still heard desperate screams echo across the water.

Lifeboat 16's passengers spent the long night searching the tumultuous (wild) seas for a rescue ship. Finally, after dawn, a ship arrived. Jessop, the infant, and all aboard Lifeboat 16 were saved.

Titanic had carried 2,223 passengers and crew, but only 706 survived. Jessop never forgot that night or those screams. Yet within two months, she was a member of the crew on another ship. She spent thirty-seven more years at sea and even survived another ship sinking.

Violet Jessop died in 1971 at age eighty-three. Even then, she loved the memories of being on the sea and the **voyages** she took on those mighty ships.

Verify Prediction

◯ CORRECT

◯ INCORRECT

Summarize

Vocabulary Review

Sentence My grandmother loves to take long ocean   to faraway places.

Sentence The soccer player made a   move, and then kicked the ball into the goal.

Sentence I saw huge   docked at a port when I went to the ocean.

Sentence My sister was   when she lost Mom's car keys.

	Active Participation	Interactive Reader	Critical Thinking Application	Week 26 Total
TOTAL POINTS FOR WEEK 26				

Stephen Hawking

A Legendary Scientist and Man

By Arden Davidson

Build Background

157

A few days before Stephen Hawking was born, his mother, Isobel, picked up a small book on astronomy at an Oxford bookshop. It would prove **prophetic.** Stephen was born January 8, 1942, exactly 300 years after the death of Galileo. No one knew then that Hawking's study of the universe would change science forever, just as Galileo's had centuries before.

There was already one scientist in the family. Stephen's father was a well-known research biologist. So it was not surprising to anyone when Stephen began showing an interest in science at a very early age. He was especially fascinated by the bees his father kept in the basement for scientific research. The fireworks his father stored in the greenhouse were off-limits. But that didn't stop a curious Stephen from trying to get to them.

Stephen was also very good at figuring out how to solve problems. He and his sister Mary spent many hours figuring out ways to get in and out of their house. He came up with eleven different escape routes in all.

Generate Questions

Stephen Hawking: A Legendary Scientist and Man

The Hawking family was a bit **eccentric.** Their car was an old London taxi. At dinner, it wasn't unusual for the family to eat in silence, while each read a favorite book. Early on, Stephen was interested in science and math. He asked constant questions about how things worked. When he was sixteen, he and his friends built a simple computer using parts from radios, clocks, and a telephone. However, he was bored in school and got just average grades.

Despite his low grades, Hawking scored so well on Oxford University's entrance exam that he was offered a scholarship to study physics at age 17. He was finally studying something he loved, and he excelled at it. In his off hours, he joined the rowing team, danced with his friends, and fell in love with the woman he would marry some years later. Hawking graduated with honors in 1962 at just twenty years of age. In post-graduate study at Cambridge, he pursued his favorite scientific field: cosmology.

Cosmology is the study of the universe. Hawking studied stars and planets and everything in outer space. His discoveries have changed our understanding of the universe and the nature of time. Hawking has written about black holes and how he thinks the universe began. He was able to explain these complicated ideas so that nonscientific people could understand them, and his books have become world-famous.

Make Prediction

Hawking's scientific accomplishments are amazing all on their own. However, they are especially **remarkable** considering that he has suffered from a terrible disease for almost fifty years. Lou Gehrig's Disease (named after a famous baseball player who suffered from it), kills nerve cells that control muscles. This affects arms, legs, the ability to speak, swallow, or breathe. Most people die three to five years after learning they have the disease.

Hawking learned he had Lou Gehrig's disease when he was twenty-one. But the diagnosis didn't slow him down. Instead, he worked even harder, thinking he had only a few years to live. Hawking taught mathematics at Cambridge University for thirty years and studied the universe from a wheelchair. For years he has not been able to move his arms or legs or to speak. He uses a computer program to speak, and assistants have helped him write numerous articles and best-selling books. He has received countless awards and honors.

Generate Questions

Stephen Hawking: A Legendary Scientist and Man

His goal, he said, is "to understand why the universe is as it is and why it exists in the first place." While no scientist has done that yet, Hawking has always thought big. Another goal is to travel into space. He got a little closer to that desire when he visited the Kennedy Space Center in Florida at the age of 65. He was able to experience an environment without **gravity.** Freed from his wheelchair, he floated in the cabin of a jet airplane speeding over the Atlantic.

Hawking even appeared in several movies and in a television episode of *Star Trek: The Next Generation.* Just as he's done all his life, he is serious about science, but he also knows how to have fun.

By his seventieth birthday in 2012, Hawking had lost all control over his body and was too weak to attend a meeting held in his honor. But in a speech written for the occasion, he said the last few decades were "a glorious time to be alive" and doing research. "Our picture of the universe has changed a great deal in the last forty years, and I am happy to have made a small contribution."

Verify Prediction

◯ CORRECT

◯ INCORRECT

Summarize

....

....

....

....

....

Vocabulary Review

Word 1

Sentence

Word 2

Sentence

Word 3

Sentence

Word 4

Sentence

TOTAL POINTS FOR WEEK 27	Active Participation	Interactive Reader	Critical Thinking Application	Week 27 Total

Stephen Hawking: A Legendary Scientist and Man

EGYPT'S REVOLUTION

By Hilary Mac Austin

Build Background

Tuesday, January 25, 2011, is a national holiday in Egypt. Thousands of people gather in Tahrir Square— Liberation Square—which is downtown in Egypt's capitol, Cairo. It is the beginning of a revolution.

In nearby Tunisia, protests have brought down the dictator of that country. Egypt is being run by a dictator also— President Hosni Mubarak, who has ruled for thirty years. Egyptians say Mubarak and his government are **corrupt.** No one is allowed to challenge the government. The police are also corrupt, and people fear them. The economy has improved, but unemployment is high, and many people are **destitute.** Protests are illegal, but Egyptians have new hope. If the people of Tunisia can change their government, maybe the people of Egypt can too.

Protestors, especially young people, have learned about the protest on Facebook and Twitter. Thousands shout, "Down with Mubarak!" At first, the protest is peaceful, but then the police charge and begin to attack the people with batons, tear gas, and water cannons. Protestors throw rocks and climb on a police truck. People are terrified, and in the past this might have stopped them. They might have gone back and hidden in their homes and criticized the government silently. Not this time. The next day, even though it is not a national holiday, even more people crowd into Tahrir Square. This time something different is happening.

Generate Questions

It is Friday, the fourth day of protests, and President Mubarak finally speaks to his people. He tells them he will create a new government, but he will not give up power himself. The people know this is not enough. They don't believe or trust Mubarak, because he has lied before. Thousands continue to protest.

On Tuesday, one week after the first day of protest, a quarter of a million people come to Tahrir Square. President Mubarak again tries to appease his people. This time he says he will not run for re-election. (There had been elections before in Egypt, but they were rigged, meaning the opposition was not allowed to participate.) Men and women, old and young, fill the square, and the men hold their shoes up in the air. They shout, "Go, go, go! We are not leaving until he leaves!" They are insulting the president, because showing the sole of a shoe is an insult in Arabic culture.

Make Prediction

Wednesday and Thursday, February 2 and 3, are days of change in the square. Pro-government protestors attack the anti-government protestors. Some think these pro-government protestors, some of whom ride into the square on horses and camels, are paid by the government. The pro-government protestors wounded and killed some of the anti-government protestors, but still the anti-government protestors won't leave. They know that if they leave the square, the revolution will be over. Men and women care for the wounded, working with nurses and doctors who have come from all over Cairo to help.

It is February 10, and the crowds have been in the square all week, night and day. It is a little like a huge party or carnival in the square. People come from all parts of Egyptian society, poor and rich, young and old, woman and man, Muslim and Christian. Muslim women in long black veils that cover their faces hold up signs and shout for freedom next to women in jeans and sunglasses. Young children wave flags as they sit on their fathers' shoulders. A group of men spell out the word *leave* with their shoes. People sing and dance, tell jokes and stories, kneel in prayer, and talk about politics and their hopes for the future.

Generate Questions

Egypt's Revolution

At the end of the day, President Mubarak gives another speech to the people in which he says he will *not* leave. The crowd had thought that Mubarak would **resign,** and they are angry. People boo and hold their shoes in the air, but still they do not become **violent,** and they do not give up, even though they may have heard that three hundred protestors have been killed.

On February 11, even more people are in Tahrir Square. At six in the evening the president makes an announcement, and a deafening roar goes up in the crowd. The president has resigned! People scream with joy while everywhere people are hugging each other. Some drop to their knees, touch their foreheads to the earth, and begin to pray. Others laugh, cry, and sing. All over Egypt, people come out of their homes and shout their happiness. They set off fireworks and wave Egyptian flags in the air. They drive around in cars and honk their horns. All over the world people watch Egypt celebrate and share its happiness. At last, they can make sure Egyptians have rights.

Those who joined the protests will never forget these eighteen days when they helped free their country. They will never forget the three hundred people who died to help set them free.

Verify Prediction

○ CORRECT

○ INCORRECT

Summarize

Vocabulary Review

Word 1

Definition

Word 2

Definition

Word 3

Definition

Word 4

Definition

	Active Participation	Interactive Reader	Critical Thinking Application	Week 28 Total
TOTAL POINTS FOR WEEK 28				

Egypt's Revolution

BE GLAD YOUR NOSE IS ON YOUR FACE

By Jack Prelutsky

Purpose for Reading

Build Background

Emotional Reaction

....
....
....
....

Rhyme

◯ YES   ◯ NO

Vocabulary

Word:

Definition:

....
....

Word:

Definition:

....
....

Word:

Definition:

....
....

Be glad your nose is on your face,
not pasted on some other place,
for if it were where it is not,
you might dislike your nose a lot.

Imagine if your precious nose
were sandwiched in between your toes,
that clearly would not be a treat,
for you'd be forced to smell your feet.

Be Glad Your Nose is on Your Face

Your nose would be a source of dread
were it attached atop your head,
it soon would drive you to **despair,**
forever tickled by your hair.

Within your ear, your nose would be
an absolute **catastrophe,**
for when you were **obliged** to sneeze,
your brain would rattle from the breeze.

Your nose, instead, through thick and thin,
remains between your eyes and chin,
not pasted on some other place—
be glad your nose is on your face!

Stanza

Theme

Speaker

○ FIRST PERSON

○ SECOND PERSON

○ THIRD PERSON

Visualization

Be Glad Your Nose is on Your Face

For this week's Readers' Theater, think about how you met each expectation. Then circle a score for each.

Expectation	I *always* did this.	I *usually* did this.	I *sometimes* did this.	I *never* did this.
I spoke clearly when it was my turn to read my lines.	4	3	2	1
I worked well with my class to practice my lines.	4	3	2	1
I listened to others so that we spoke together on group lines.	4	3	2	1
I highlighted my lines so I knew when to speak.	4	3	2	1
I held the script so people could hear me (I didn't hide behind the script or look at the floor).	4	3	2	1
I used my voice to help people understand the poem.	4	3	2	1

	Active Participation	Interactive Reader	Critical Thinking Application	Week 29 Total
TOTAL POINTS FOR WEEK 29				

Be Glad Your Nose is on Your Face

SOME WORDS ABOUT TIME

By Gary Soto

Purpose for Reading

Build Background

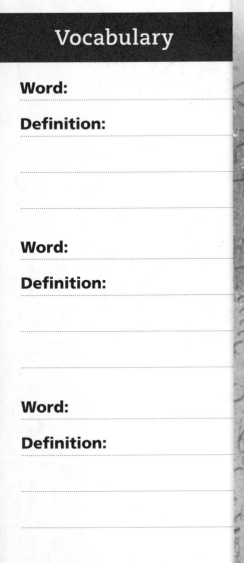

Word:

Definition:

Word:

Definition:

Word:

Definition:

Bored, I open the back of an ancient clock
And the minutes pile out,
Exhausted from spinning
Out the same hammered seconds.
The minutes **stagger** on the table
And collapse, for they are dizzy,
For they have realized they have no legs,
For the surface of the table is flat
And what have they known but a round world.
I touch one of the minutes—an ant
With feeling antennae—
and with my hand
Bulldoze them all to the kitchen floor.

Again, I am bored. I examine the oily guts
of the clock, tinker with the sprockets
And springs, and **revel** in the master plan
To keep **lackeys** punching the clock.
I think of myself at the car wash
Bringing a soapy sponge to
The toothy grill of an old Pontiac.

I used four seconds on each of the
dirty teeth,
And ten seconds on each droopy headlight.
This was how I viewed time
At age seventeen, the boy in morning
Sunlight and, two minutes to eight,
Reaching for a sponge,
Sponge that was a wheezing lung—
Even before the clock started
My hand struggled with an exhausted tool.

Speaker

- ○ FIRST PERSON
- ○ SECOND PERSON
- ○ THIRD PERSON

Visualization

Some Words about Time

For this week's Readers' Theater, think about how you met each expectation. Then circle a score for each.

Expectation	I *always* did this.	I *usually* did this.	I *sometimes* did this.	I *never* did this.
I spoke clearly when it was my turn to read my lines.	4	3	2	1
I worked well with my class to practice my lines.	4	3	2	1
I listened to others so that we spoke together on group lines.	4	3	2	1
I highlighted my lines so I knew when to speak.	4	3	2	1
I held the script so people could hear me (I didn't hide behind the script or look at the floor).	4	3	2	1
I used my voice to help people understand the poem.	4	3	2	1

	Active Participation	Interactive Reader	Critical Thinking Application	Week 30 Total
TOTAL POINTS FOR WEEK 30				

THOSE FABULOUS FRENCHMEN

By Joyce Sidman

Etienne & Josep[h]
MONTGOLFI[ER]

Purpose for Reading

Build Background

Vocabulary

Word:

Definition:

Word:

Definition:

Word:

Definition:

They played around a lot with fire,
Joe and Jacques Montgolfier—
set the harvest grass alight
and watched the blue smoke whirl away.

One of them—we're not sure which—
to feed the dying **embers,** chose
to burn an empty paper bag.
It filled with blackened air and rose!

They tried again, experimented,
and, perfecting their balloon,
they launched a duck into the air
above Versailles one afternoon.

Those Fabulous Frenchmen

It worked! And shortly after that,
Jacques Charles, another Frenchman, found
a lovely gas called hydrogen
would take him farther off the ground.

Then there was Jean-Pierre Blanchard,
who, not content to merely float
across the English Channel, used
two silken oars to steer his "boat"!

He made it, by some miracle,
and gay Paree went balloon-mad.
Many flew and many crashed
amid this aeronautic fad.

Balloons? They've gone the way of horses:
cumbersome and rather rare,
but they were first to lift us up
into the bright, enchanted air.

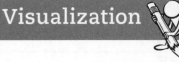

Speaker

- ◯ FIRST PERSON
- ◯ SECOND PERSON
- ◯ THIRD PERSON

Visualization

Etienne & Joseph
MONTGOLFIER

Self-Evaluation

For this week's Readers' Theater, think about how you met each expectation. Then circle a score for each.

Expectation	I *always* did this.	I *usually* did this.	I *sometimes* did this.	I *never* did this.
I spoke clearly when it was my turn to read my lines.	4	3	2	1
I worked well with my class to practice my lines.	4	3	2	1
I listened to others so that we spoke together on group lines.	4	3	2	1
I highlighted my lines so I knew when to speak.	4	3	2	1
I held the script so people could hear me (I didn't hide behind the script or look at the floor).	4	3	2	1
I used my voice to help people understand the poem.	4	3	2	1

	Active Participation	Interactive Reader	Critical Thinking Application	Week 31 Total
TOTAL POINTS FOR WEEK 31				

Those Fabulous Frenchmen

I LOVE THE LOOK OF WORDS

By Maya Angelou

POP!

Perfuming

butter

CHOMP

fresh POP CORN DELICIOUS

Purpose for Reading

Build Background

Popcorn leaps, popping from the floor
of a hot black skillet
and into my mouth.
Black words leap,
snapping from the white
page. Rushing into my eyes. Sliding
into my brain which **gobbles** them
the way my tongue and teeth
chomp the buttered popcorn.

Rhyme

○ YES   ○ NO

Vocabulary

Word:

Definition:

Word:

Definition:

Word:

Definition:

When I have stopped reading,
ideas from the words stay stuck
in my mind, like the sweet
smell of butter **perfuming** my
fingers long after the popcorn is finished.

I love the book and the look of words
the weight of ideas that popped into
my mind
I love the tracks
of new thinking in my mind.

I Love the Look of Words

Stanza

Theme

Speaker

◯ **FIRST PERSON**

◯ **SECOND PERSON**

◯ **THIRD PERSON**

Visualization

Self-Evaluation

For this week's Readers' Theater, think about how you met each expectation. Then circle a score for each.

Expectation	I *always* did this.	I *usually* did this.	I *sometimes* did this.	I *never* did this.
I spoke clearly when it was my turn to read my lines.	4	3	2	1
I worked well with my class to practice my lines.	4	3	2	1
I listened to others so that we spoke together on group lines.	4	3	2	1
I highlighted my lines so I knew when to speak.	4	3	2	1
I held the script so people could hear me (I didn't hide behind the script or look at the floor).	4	3	2	1
I used my voice to help people understand the poem.	4	3	2	1

	Active Participation	Interactive Reader	Critical Thinking Application	Week 32 Total
TOTAL POINTS FOR WEEK 32				

I Love the Look of Words

Reading Log

Name _____ **Date** _____

Start date	End date	Title	Author	How would you rate this book? Why?

Reading Log

Name _____ **Date** _____

Start date	End date	Title	Author	How would you rate this book? Why?

Glossary

Use this glossary to pronounce and understand the meanings of the vocabulary words. The part of speech, such as *adj.* for **adjective** or *v.* for **verb,** shows how the vocabulary word is used in the selection it appears in. Page numbers in parentheses tell where to find the word in your Interactive Reader.

A

account (ə **kownt**) *n.* a report of something that happened (p. 64)

admire (əd **mir**) *v.* to like very much, be impressed (p. 17)

advanced (əd **vansd**) *adj.* farther ahead than the average (p. 93)

advertising (**ad** vur tī zing) *adj.* paid announcements to call attention to something (p. 118)

alarming (ə **lor** ming) *adj.* frightening (p. 105)

amid (ə **mid**) *prep.* In the middle of (p. 179)

astounded (ə **stown** dəd) *v.* amazed, astonished (p. 112)

B

bargain (**bar** gən) *n.* an agreement or deal (p. 87)

barrier (**ba** rē ər) *n.* something that blocks or keeps things out (p. 106)

baton (bə **ton**) *n.* long, thin rod (p. 38)

beheaded (bə **he** dəd) *v.* had head cut off (p. 70)

bristles (**bri** səlz) *n.* short, stiff threads or hairs (p. 100)

business (**biz** nis) *n.* a concern, a private matter (p. 15)

Pronunciation Key

The following symbols are used throughout this glossary.

a	ask	e	bed	o	over	ow	now	ə	about
ā	ate		bread	u	but		about		kitten
	eight	i	it		what	oy	boy		Canada
	pain	ī	ice		other		oil		lemon
ē	pizza		tie	aw	awful	oo	book		circus
	each		why		ball		pull		wanted
	mini	o	on		auto	o͞o	pool		
	many		father		soft		blue		
	feet		not						

Syllables that are underlined and in bold are stressed the most, such as **ak** in **reaction** (rē **ak** shun).

Syllables that are stressed a little but not as much as another syllable are in bold, such as **shun** in **reaction.**

Glossary

C

catastrophe (kə **ta** strə fē) *n.* a terrible event (p. 171)

chomp (chomp) *v.* bite hard (p. 182)

clone (klōn) *v.* make an exact copy of a living thing using its DNA (p. 146)

coma (**kō** mə) *n.* a deep sleep caused by an injury (p. 63)

compulsory (kəm **pul** sə rē) *adj.* required by law (p. 116)

confident (**kon** fi dənt) *adj.* sure of yourself, knowing you are right (p. 52)

confirmed (kən **furmd**) *v.* made stronger (p. 77)

corrupt (kə **rupt**) *adj.* dishonest in return for money or personal gain (p. 164)

crime (krīm) *n.* an activity that's against the law (p. 124)

cumbersome (**kum** bər səm) *adj.* hard to handle or use (p. 179)

D

despair (di **spār**) *n.* sadness (p. 171)

despite (di **spīt**) *prep.* aside from, regardless of (p. 134)

destitute (**de** sti **tōōt**) *adj.* poor enough to need help from others for basic needs (p. 164)

diagnosed (**dī** əg **nōst**) *v.* told what illness you have (p. 9)

disaster (di **za** stər) *n.* something horrible that causes suffering and pain (p. 82)

ditch (dich) *v.* hide, get rid of (p. 51)

divulge (də **vulj**) *v.* to tell, make known (p. 135)

dodging (**do** jing) *v.* getting away from, avoiding (p. 110)

doubtful (**dowt** fəl) *adj.* unsure, not likely, not believing (p. 99)

dwelled (dweld) *v.* lived in (p. 122)

E

eccentric (ik **sen** trik) *adj.* strange, odd, or unusual (p. 159)

embers (**em** bərz) *n.* glowing ashes left after a fire (p. 178)

ensues (in **sōōz**) *v.* takes place or happens as a result (p. 140)

envy (**en** vē) *n.* the feeling of wanting something that belongs to another (p. 3)

escapable (e **scā** pə bəl) *adj.* possible to avoid or get away from (p. 71)

exuberant (ig **zōō** bə rint) *adj.* filled with lively energy (p. 123)

F

facets (<u>fa</u> sets) *n.* small, flat surfaces on a jewel (p. 69)

fainted (<u>fān</u> təd) *v.* suddenly passed out (p. 5)

farces (<u>far</u> səs) *n.* funny plays about ridiculous things (p. 23)

fate (fāt) *n.* what might happen in the future (p. 23)

footage (<u>foo</u> təj) *n.* a recording on video or film (p. 82)

frantic (<u>fran</u> tik) *adj.* wild with worry and fear (p. 154)

function (<u>fungk</u> shən) *v.* to do something, to work (p. 62)

G

gobbles (<u>go</u> bəlz) *v.* eats quickly (p. 182)

gravity (<u>gra</u> və tē) *n.* a force in nature that pulls things toward Earth (p. 161)

H

harried (<u>ha</u> rēd) *adj.* stressed, worried and anxious (p. 136)

heap (hēp) *n.* a lot, very much (p. 88)

heartily (<u>hor</u> tə lē) *adv.* in an enthusiastic and energetic way (p. 124)

heiresses (<u>e</u> ri səz) *n.* women who inherit a lot of money and wealth (p. 68)

I

inhabit (in <u>ha</u> bət) *v.* live in (p. 149)

intact (in <u>takt</u>) *adj.* in one piece, whole, not damaged or broken (p. 147)

intense (in <u>tens</u>) *adj.* extreme, powerful (p. 28)

investor (in <u>ves</u> tər) *n.* a person who gives money to a company in order to get more money back (p. 119)

irritable (<u>i</u> ri tə bəl) *adj.* easy to make angry (p. 65)

J

jabbed (jabd) *v.* pushed at, poked (p. 95)

L

lackeys (<u>la</u> kēz) *n.* low-level workers, laborers (p. 175)

legacy (<u>le</u> gə sē) *n.* anything that is passed down from someone who came before (p. 107)

levees (<u>le</u> vēz) *n.* long walls built near a body of water to prevent flooding (p. 81)

longed (lawngd) *v.* wished (p. 86)

Glossary

M

mainstream (<u>mān</u> strēm) *adj.* usual, ordinary, accepting the current ideas (p. 128)

manipulating (mə <u>ni</u> pyoo <u>lā</u> ting) *v.* changing, moving (p. 148)

mere (mēr) *adj.* very little, small amount (p. 2)

mobbed (mobd) *adj.* crowded with people (p. 56)

modern (<u>mo</u> dərn) *adj.* new; from recent times (p. 34)

murmurs (<u>mur</u> mərs) *v.* whispers quietly (p. 44)

N

nimble (<u>nim</u> bəl) *adj.* quick and easy in movement (p. 153)

O

obliged (ə <u>blojd</u>) *v.* forced to do something (p. 171)

P

perfuming (pər <u>fyoo</u> ming) *v.* filling with a nice smell (p. 182)

plague (plāg) *n.* disease that spreads quickly and causes many deaths (p. 20)

potentially (pə <u>ten</u> shə lē) *adv.* possibly (p. 77)

predators (<u>pre</u> də tərz) *n.* animals that live by killing and eating other animals (p. 74)

prefer (pri <u>fur</u>) *v.* like better (p. 8)

prejudice (<u>pre</u> jə dis) *n.* unfair feeling about someone based on looks, race, or religion (p. 27)

privileges (<u>priv</u> li jəz) *n.* benefits or rights that other people don't get (p. 59)

promoted (prə <u>mō</u> təd) *v.* helped someone or something become known (p. 40)

prophetic (prə <u>fe</u> tik) *adj.* having to do with future events (p. 158)

propped (propt) *v.* put an object against something to keep it from falling (p. 88)

pruning (<u>prū</u> ning) *adj.* used for trimming branches (p. 50)

R

reaction (rē <u>ak shun</u>) *n.* the look or feeling someone has after something happens (p. 4)

reign (rān) *n.* time period a royal person rules (p. 32)

remarkable (ri <u>mar</u> kə bəl) *adj.* unusual, worthy of being noticed (p. 160)

residence (<u>re</u> sə dəns) *n.* place where someone lives (p. 52)

resign (rə <u>zīn</u>) *v.* voluntarily leave a job (p. 167)

revel (<u>re</u> vəl) *v.* enjoy greatly (p. 175)

ritziest (<u>rit</u> zē əst) *adj.* fanciest (p. 129)

S

sanctuary (<u>sangk chu</u> e rē) protection in a safe place (p. 111)

sarcastic (sor <u>kas</u> tik) *adj.* using harsh or bitter words that say one thing but mean another (p. 130)

scolded (<u>skōl</u> dəd) *v.* criticized a person angrily for doing something wrong (p. 98)

skillet (<u>ski</u> lət) *n.* a frying pan (p. 100)

sneak preview (snēk <u>prē</u> vyo͞o) *n.* a special showing of something before others see it (p. 59)

sniper (<u>snī</u> pur) *n.* person who shoots others from a hiding place (p. 26)

solidify (sə <u>li</u> də <u>fī</u>) *v.* become hard and unmovable (p. 11)

stabilize (<u>stā</u> bə <u>līz</u>) *v.* make something less likely to fall over (p. 11)

stagger (<u>sta</u> gər) *v.* move unsteadily from side to side (p. 174)

sterilized (<u>ste</u> rə līzd) *v.* cleaned so all germs are destroyed (p. 104)

still (stil) *adj.* not moving (p. 17)

stirred (stuhrd) *v.* caused strong feelings that moved people to action (p. 113)

stubborn (<u>stu</u> bərn) *adj.* refusing to change or do something (p. 15)

summon (<u>su</u> mən) *v.* to call for, to send for

symptoms (<u>simp</u> təms) *n.* signs of an illness (p. 21)

T

tactics (<u>tak</u> tiks) *n.* plans, planned action

territory (<u>te</u> ri <u>to</u> rē) *n.* area of land belonging to a government (p. 40)

tolerate (<u>to</u> lə <u>rāt</u>) *v.* put up with, allow (p. 141)

tomb (to͞om) *n.* place where a dead body is kept (p. 33)

torched (torcht) *v.* set on fire (p. 47)

traditional (trə <u>di</u> shu nəl) *adj.* done by a specific group of people for a long time (p. 39)

triumphs (<u>trī</u> umfs) *n.* important achievements (p. 29)

tycoon (tī <u>ko͞on</u>) *n.* a wealthy businessperson (p. 131)

U

unemployed (un im <u>ployd</u>) *adj.* without a job (p. 116)

updraft (<u>up</u> draft) *n.* a strong, upward current of air (p. 44)

upgraded (<u>up</u> grā dəd) *v.* got a higher rating, boosted (p. 81)

Glossary

V

venom (**ve** nəm) *n.* poison made by an animal that can injure or kill (p. 74)

vessels (**ve** səlz) *n.* large boats or ships (p. 152)

violent (**vī** ə lənt) *adj.* using physical force to hurt someone or something (p. 167)

voyages (**voy** əj əz) *n.* long journeys or trips (p. 155)

W

wading (**wā** ding) *n.* walking through shallow water (p. 94)

warrior (**wo** ri ər) *n.* person who fights in battles (p. 34)

wheezing (**wē** zing) *n.* the sound of breathing with difficulty (p. 47)

whisks (wisks) *v.* moves quickly (p. 137)

wing (wing) *n.* hall or area off the main part of a building (p. 56)

wrinkled (**ring** kəld) *adj.* creased, had little lines and folds (p. 93)

Acknowledgements

Reprinted with the permission of Simon & Schuster Books for Young Readers, an imprint of Simon & Schuster Children's Publishing Division from ANYTHING BUT TYPICAL by Nora Raleigh Baskin. Copyright © 2009 Nora Raleigh Baskin.

Excerpts taken from the book LISTENING FOR CRICKETS by David Gifaldi. Copyright © 2008 by David Gifaldi. Reprinted by permission of Henry Holt and Company, LLC.

Reprinted from THE GREAT CHICKEN DEBACLE by Phyllis Reynolds Naylor with permission of Marshall Cavendish.

Excerpt from LILY B. ON THE BRINK OF COOL Text copyright © 2006 by Elizabeth Cody Kimmel. All rights reserved. Used with permission of Wernick & Pratt Agency, LLC.

"Be Glad Your Nose Is on Your Face" from THE NEW KID ON THE BLOCK by Jack Prelutsky. Text copyright © 1984 by Jack Prelutsky. Used by permission of HarperCollins Publishers.

"Some Words about Time" © 2005 by Gary Soto. Used by permission of the author.

"Those Fabulous Frenchmen" poem by Joyce Sidman, from EUREKA! POEMS ABOUT INVENTORS. Text copyright © 2002 by Joyce Sidman. Reprinted with the permission of Millbrook Press, a division of Lerner Publishing Group, Inc. All rights reserved. No part of this text excerpt may be used or reproduced in any manner whatsoever without the prior written permission of Lerner Publishing Group, Inc.

"I Love the Look of Words (text)" by Maya Angelou, copyright © 1993 by Maya Angelou, from SOUL LOOKS BACK IN WONDER by Tom Feelings. Used by permission of Dial Books for Young Readers, A Division of Penguin Young Readers Group, A Member of Penguin Group (USA) Inc., 345 Hudson Street, New York, NY 10014. All rights reserved.

Credits

COVER (t) Siede Preis/Photodisc/Getty Images; (tl) Brand X Pictures/PunchStock; c) Digital Vision/PunchStock; (b) Ingram Publishing; 1 (l) PhotoLink/Photodisc/Getty Images, (r)DEA PICTURE LIBRARY/De Agostini Picture Library/Getty Images, (b)Anna Williams/Stockbyte/Getty Images; 3 PhotoLink/Photodisc/Getty Images; 5 DEA PICTURE LIBRARY/De Agostini Picture Library/Getty Images; 7 (t)Thinkstock/Getty Images, (c) Image Source/Getty Images, (r)Jupiterimages/Comstock Images/Getty Images, (b)Anna Williams/Stockbyte/Getty Images, (b)OJO Images/Getty Images; 9 Jupiterimages/Comstock Images/Getty Images, (bkgd) Thinkstock/Getty Images; 10 11 OJO Images/Getty Images; 13 (l) BananaStock/PictureQuest, (r)Jupiterimages/Comstock Images/Getty Images, (b)Anna Williams/Stockbyte/Getty Images, (bkgd)Gary Moss Photography/Photographer's Choice/Getty Images; 15 (l)Gary Moss Photography/Photographer's Choice/Getty Images, (r)Jupiterimages/Comstock Images/Getty Images; 16 BananaStock/PictureQuest; 17 Gary Moss Photography/Photographer's Choice/Getty Images; 19 (l)Ingram Publishing/Alamy, (r)Pixtal/age fotostock, (b)Anna Williams/Stockbyte/Getty Images, (bkgd)Inti St. Clair/Photodisc/Getty Images; 21 (l)Inti St. Clair/Photodisc/Getty Images, (r)Pixtal/age fotostock; 22 Pixtal/age fotostock; 23 Ingram Publishing/Alamy; 25 (l)Photos 12/Alamy, (c)Paul Thompson/War Department/National Archives/Time Life Pictures/Getty Images, (r)FPG/Archive Photos/Getty Images, (b)Anna Williams/Stockbyte/Getty Images; 27 (t)FPG/Archive Photos/Getty Images, (b)Paul Thompson/War Department/National Archives/Time Life Pictures/Getty Images; 28 Photos 12/Alamy; 31 (l)DEA PICTURE LIBRARY/De Agostini Picture Library/Getty Images, (r)Mansell/Time & Life Pictures/Getty Images, (b) Anna Williams/Stockbyte/Getty Images; 33 DEA PICTURE LIBRARY/De Agostini Picture Library/Getty Images; 35 Mansell/Time & Life Pictures/Getty Images; 37 (t)UVimages/amanaimages/Corbis, (c)Goss Images/Alamy, (b)Anna Williams/Stockbyte/Getty Images, (b)Antenna Audio, Inc./Getty Images; 39 (l)Antenna Audio, Inc./Getty Images, (r)Goss Images/Alamy; 40 Goss Images/Alamy; 41 Antenna Audio, Inc./Getty Images; 43 (t)Howard Kingsnorth/Taxi/Getty Images, (b)Anna Williams/Stockbyte/Getty Images, (bl br)Photodisc/Getty Images; 44 45 46 Photodisc/Getty Images; 47 (t)Photodisc/Getty Images, (b)Howard Kingsnorth/Taxi/Getty Images; 49 (l)Ingram Publishing/Fotosearch, (r)Stockdisc/PunchStock, (b)Anna Williams/Stockbyte/Getty Images, (br)Photodisc/Getty Images; 50 Ingram Publishing/Fotosearch; 52 Photodisc/Getty Images; 53 Stockdisc/PunchStock; 55 (l c)Ingram Publishing/SuperStock, (r)Toru Sanogawa/iStock Vectors/Getty Images, (b)Anna Williams/Stockbyte/Getty Images, (bl br)Photodisc/Getty Images; 56 Ingram Publishing/SuperStock; 58 Photodisc/Getty Images; 59 Toru Sanogawa/iStock Vectors/Getty Images; 61 (l)Patrick Byrd/Alamy, (r)Everett Collection Inc/Alamy, (b)Anna Williams/Stockbyte/Getty Images, (bkgd)Ingram Publishing/SuperStock; 62 Everett Collection Inc/Alamy; 63 (l)Patrick Byrd/Alamy, (r)Ingram Publishing/SuperStock; 64 65 Ingram Publishing/SuperStock; 67 (l)PAUL J. RICHARDS/AFP/Getty Images, (r)Topical Press Agency/Hulton Archive/Getty Images, (b)Anna Williams/Stockbyte/Getty Images, (bkgd)Dorling Kindersley/Getty Images; 69 (l)PAUL J. RICHARDS/AFP/Getty Images, (r)Topical Press Agency/Hulton Archive/Getty Images; 71 Dorling Kindersley/Getty Images; 73 (tc)William Leaman/Alamy, (tl tr cr bl br)Harold G. Scott (photographer)/Centers for Disease Control and Prevention, (b)Anna Williams/Stockbyte/Getty Images, (br)Markus Guhl/Photodisc/Getty Images, (bkgd)ZUMA Wire Service/Alamy; 74 Harold G. Scott (photographer)/Centers for Disease Control and Prevention; 75 (l)Harold G. Scott (photographer)/Centers for Disease Control and Prevention, (t) ZUMA Wire Service/Alamy, (b)William Leaman/Alamy; 76 Harold G. Scott (photographer)/Centers for Disease Control and Prevention; 77 (l r) Harold G. Scott (photographer)/Centers for Disease Control and Prevention, (c)Markus Guhl/Photodisc/Getty Images; 79 (l)Burke/Triolo/ Brand X Pictures/Jupiterimages, (c)Julie Dermansky/Corbis, (r)Skip Bolen/Getty Images Entertainment/Getty Images, (b)Anna Williams/Stockbyte/Getty Images, (b)Antenna Audio, Inc./Getty Images; 81 (l)Burke/Triolo/Brand X Pictures/Jupiterimages, (r)Skip Bolen/Getty Images

Entertainment/Getty Images; 82 Julie Dermansky/Corbis; 85 (l)Siede Preis/Photodisc/Getty Images, (t)imac/Alamy, (c)CMCD/Photodisc/Getty Images, (r)Ingram Publishing/SuperStock, (b)Anna Williams/Stockbyte/Getty Images; 87 Siede Preis/Photodisc/Getty Images; 88 Ingram Publishing/SuperStock; 89 imac/Alamy; 91 (l)Siede Preis/Photodisc/Getty Images, (t) Emmet Malmstrom/Photodisc/Getty Images, (c)CMCD/Photodisc/Getty Images, (r)IT Stock Free/Alamy, (b)Anna Williams/Stockbyte/Getty Images; 93 Siede Preis/Photodisc/Getty Images; 94 IT Stock Free/Alamy; 95 Emmet Malmstrom/Photodisc/Getty Images; 97 (l)Siede Preis/Photodisc/Getty Images, (t)Ingram Publishing, (r)CMCD/Photodisc/Getty Images, (b)Anna Williams/Stockbyte/Getty Images; 99 Siede Preis/Photodisc/Getty Images; 100 CMCD/Photodisc/Getty Images; 101 Ingram Publishing; 103 (l) Bettmann/Corbis, (r)Brand X Pictures/PunchStock, (b)Anna Williams/Stockbyte/Getty Images, (bkgd)Everett Collection Inc/Alamy; 104 Bettmann/Corbis; 105 Everett Collection Inc/Alamy; 107 Brand X Pictures/PunchStock; 109 (l)Ingram Publishing/Fotosearch, (r)Buyenlarge/Archive Photos/Getty Images, (b)Anna Williams/Stockbyte/Getty Images; 111 Ingram Publishing/Fotosearch; 113 Buyenlarge/Archive Photos/Getty Images; 115 (l)Ingram Publishing, (c)WoodyStock/Alamy, (r)William Andrew/Photographer's Choice/Getty Images, (b)Anna Williams/Stockbyte/Getty Images, (bkgd)Craig P. Jewell/Flickr/Getty Images; 116 Ingram Publishing; 117 (t)WoodyStock/Alamy, (b)Craig P. Jewell/Flickr/Getty Images; 119 (r)William Andrew/Photographer's Choice/Getty Images, (bkgd)Craig P. Jewell/Flickr/Getty Images; 121 (t)Marilyn Nieves/Vetta/Getty Images, (b)Anna Williams/Stockbyte/Getty Images, (bkgd) Joseph Shields/Photolibrary/Getty Images; 123 Marilyn Nieves/Vetta/Getty Images; 125 Joseph Shields/Photolibrary/Getty Images; 127 (l) Rubberball/Jessica Peterson/Getty Images, (r)J. Hardy/PhotoAlto, (b)Anna Williams/Stockbyte/Getty Images, (bl)McGraw-Hill Companies, Inc. Ken Karp, photographer; 129 (l)McGraw-Hill Companies, Inc. Ken Karp, photographer, (r)J. Hardy/PhotoAlto; 131 Rubberball/Jessica Peterson/Getty Images; 133 (l)Maria Toutoudaki/Digital Vision/Getty Images, (r)J. Hardy/PhotoAlto, (b)Anna Williams/Stockbyte/Getty Images, (bl) McGraw-Hill Companies, Inc. Ken Karp, photographer; 135 (l)McGraw-Hill Companies, Inc. Ken Karp, photographer, (r)J. Hardy/PhotoAlto; 137 Maria Toutoudaki/Digital Vision/Getty Images; 139 (l)Stockbyte/PunchStock, (r)J. Hardy/PhotoAlto, (b)Anna Williams/Stockbyte/Getty Images, (bl)McGraw-Hill Companies, Inc. Ken Karp, photographer; 141 (l) McGraw-Hill Companies, Inc. Ken Karp, photographer, (r)J. Hardy/PhotoAlto; 143 Stockbyte/PunchStock; 145 (c)John Elk III/Alamy, (b)Anna Williams/Stockbyte/Getty Images, (bl br)Hank Grebe/Purestock/Getty Images, (br)Hank Grebe/Purestock/Getty Images, (bkgd)Peter Dazeley/Stone/Getty Images; 147 (t)Peter Dazeley/Stone/Getty Images, (b)John Elk III/Alamy; 148 Hank Grebe/Purestock/Getty Images; 149 Hank Grebe/Purestock/Getty Images; 151 (l t)Classic Image/Alamy, (r)World History Archive/Alamy, (b)Anna Williams/Stockbyte/Getty Images; 153 154 Classic Image/Alamy; 155 Stockbyte/Getty Images; 157 (l)Purestock/SuperStock, (t)Brand X Pictures/PunchStock, (r)David Montgomery/Hulton Archive/Getty Images, (b)Anna Williams/Stockbyte/Getty Images, (bl)RIA NOVOSTI/Science Photo Library/Getty Images; 159 (t)Brand X Pictures/PunchStock, (r)David Montgomery/Hulton Archive/Getty Images, (b)RIA NOVOSTI/Science Photo Library/Getty Images; 160 Brand X Pictures/PunchStock; 161 (t)Purestock/SuperStock, (b)Brand X Pictures/PunchStock; 163 (l r)Peter Macdiarmid/Getty Images News/Getty Images, (c)FILIPPO MONTEFORTE/AFP/Getty Images, (b)Anna Williams/Stockbyte/Getty Images; 165 FILIPPO MONTEFORTE/AFP/Getty Images; 166 Peter Macdiarmid/Getty Images News/Getty Images; 167 Peter Macdiarmid/Getty Images News/Getty Images; 169 Anna Williams/Stockbyte/Getty Images; 173 (l)Comstock Images/Jupiterimages, (b)Anna Williams/Stockbyte/Getty Images; 175 Comstock Images/Jupiterimages; 177 (l) Science & Society Picture Library/SSPL/Getty Images, (r)Burke/Triolo/Brand X Pictures/Jupiterimages; 179 (l)Science & Society Picture Library/SSPL/Getty Images, (r)Burke/Triolo/Brand X Pictures/Jupiterimages; 181 (l)D. Hurst/Alamy, (b)Anna Williams/Alamy.